# INGRES

## CENTENNIAL EXHIBITION

### 1867–1967

⊱ ⊱ DRAWINGS, WATERCOLORS AND OIL

SKETCHES FROM AMERICAN COLLECTIONS ·

FOGG ART MUSEUM, HARVARD UNIVERSITY

FEBRUARY 12 – APRIL 9, 1967 ⊱ ⊱ ⊱ ⊱

FRONT COVER: *Portrait of Madame Hayard and her Daughter Caroline*, 1815 (No. 28)

FRONTISPIECE: Pierre-Jean David, called David d'Angers, *Profile Portrait Medallions of Monsieur and Madame Ingres*, 1826, Fogg Art Museum, Harvard University, Bequest of Grenville L. Winthrop

BACK COVER: *View of the Villa Medici, Rome*, 1807, detail (No. 7)

# TABLE OF CONTENTS

# LIST OF LENDERS

Anonymous, 24, 34, 43, 51, 77

Mr. Curtis Baer, New York, New York, 91

Mrs. George F. Baker, Locust Valley, New York, 67

Mr. Walter C. Baker, New York, New York, 44, 45, 57

Mr. John Nicholas Brown, Providence, Rhode Island, 49

Mrs. Elizabeth Paine Card, Boston, Massachusetts, 72

Estate of Nathan J. Cohn, Spring Valley, New York, 102, 111

Mr. Stephen R. Currier, New York, New York, 62

Mr. David Daniels, New York, New York, 71

Mr. John Goelet, New York, New York, 11, 16

Mr. Roger S. Guerber, White Plains, New York, 80, 81, 82

Mrs. Jacob M. Kaplan, New York, New York, 8

Mrs. Hugh Kirkland, Santa Barbara, California, 64

Mrs. Albert D. Lasker, New York, New York, 92

Mr. Robert Lehman, New York, New York, 25, 42, 100

Dr. James H. Lockhart, Jr., Geneseo, New York, 46

Mrs. Richard C. Paine, Boston, Massachusetts, 69

Mr. and Mrs. Benjamin Sonnenberg, New York, New York, 105

Mrs. Mark C. Steinberg, St. Louis, Missouri, 39

Mr. Chauncey Stillman, New York, New York, 70

Mrs. Herbert N. Straus, New York, New York, 30

Mrs. Jesse I. Straus, New York, New York, 37

Mr. John S. Thacher, Washington, D. C., 29

Mr. and Mrs. Eugene Victor Thaw, New York, New York, 101

Mr. and Mrs. John N. Warrington, Cincinnati, Ohio, 88

Mrs. Douglas Williams, New York, New York, 94

Mr. Ian Woodner, New York, New York, 76

# INTRODUCTION

EXACTLY ONE HUNDRED YEARS AGO, the first page of the February number of the *Gazette des Beaux-Arts* announced to the art world, *"Ingres est mort."* Within a heavy black border, the announcement continued, "... (it is) an irreparable loss which every passing day will make more perceptible." It closed with the prophecy that Ingres would have a place in history as long as a single one of his masterpieces survived. The tribute was signed by the learned and perceptive Émile Galichon, one of the finest connoisseurs of the nineteenth century, who was then the *Gazette*'s editor.

A few months later a great memorial exhibition of Ingres' work was held at the École des Beaux-Arts, the school which Ingres had entered as a student in 1799 and where he had held the rank of Professor from December, 1829, until his resignation in October, 1851. In that Memorial Exhibition nearly six hundred works were shown. No comparable exhibition has been held since. Indeed, one wonders if it would be possible ever again to assemble an exhibition of equal variety and importance, so widely scattered are the works, so insuperable certain difficulties. Twenty-three of the drawings that were in that exhibition are in the present one.

Six years before, in 1861, which was, as it happened, just six years after the Exposition Universelle at which a special pavilion had been devoted to the work of Ingres, there was a less ambitious exhibition at the Salon des Arts-Unis. Assembled by his admirers, it had contained only drawings. There were ninety-two entries. Henri Delaborde, who was to publish in 1870 the first serious monograph devoted to the work of Ingres, reviewed the 1861 exhibition in the pages of the *Gazette des Beaux-Arts*. In giving great praise to the work of Ingres, who was of course then still alive, he wrote that he feared neither scorn from his contemporaries nor contradiction in the future, for he was only anticipating the judgment of history. Like La Bruyère in another context, he was speaking in advance the language of posterity.

Galichon shared this opinion so strongly that he felt it incumbent upon himself to do for that posterity what he wished contemporary critics had done for the drawings of earlier great masters, that was to record "the purpose, the provenance and the history" of the ninety-two drawings shown. He divided them into groups and discussed the different drawings in each group. It is the earliest critical and careful commentary on Ingres' drawings. Clairvoyant though Galichon was, he could hardly have foreseen how grateful to him we would be a hundred years later.

If, compared to the exhibition of 1867, our present one seems modest, it is somewhat more ambitious than the one of 1861, for it is one quarter larger. Sixteen drawings shown today (only ten of which had been in the 1867 exhibition) were at the Salons des Arts-Unis in 1861. These surely had the blessing of the master himself, for it is inconceivable that they could have been exhibited in his presence without his approval.

On this side of the Atlantic, the Fogg Art Museum seems the logical place in which to mark the one hundredth anniversary of Ingres' death. Over sixty-five of his works belong to the Fogg

Museum. The majority came in 1943 in the magnificent bequest of Grenville L. Winthrop. One of the conditions of that bequest was that no part of it could be lent beyond the confines of the University. The rigid stipulation against our lending might have had an adverse effect when we asked to borrow had our friends been less understanding. In fact, collectors and museum colleagues have been extraordinarily generous on this occasion. We are deeply grateful to them. We have tried to show our gratitude by publishing in this catalogue wherever possible, relevant data about each drawing, much of which has not hitherto been known. In this project we have been most ably and generously assisted by Dr. Hans Naef who came under a special grant from Switzerland to work with us and who has put the results of his many years of archival research regarding the portrait drawings completely at our disposal.

Since the Fogg Museum is a university museum with limited gallery space and a restricted budget, we decided to confine our choice of works for the exhibition to drawings, watercolors and a few oil sketches. It would have been difficult, if not impossible, to have shown paintings which would have illuminated the full range of his subject matter and the development of his style. The six paintings which came to the Fogg Museum with the Winthrop Bequest will be on view during the exhibition although they are not, technically, part of it. They are the *Raphael and the Fornarina* (1814), the *Portrait of M. de Nogent* (1818), the *Odalisque with the Slave* (1839), the *Portrait of Hortense Reiset* (1844), the *Self-Portrait* (1859) and the reduced replica of the *Golden Age* (1862). Four letters by Ingres in the possession of the Houghton Library, Harvard University, will also be exhibited.

We have not attempted to be all-inclusive. There are a number of distinguished drawings by Ingres in American collections for which we have not asked. Our aim has not been completeness, but rather to show the graphic style of the artist from his earliest to his last years and to reveal his highly personal use of a variety of media. This is one of the reasons for the Technical Appendix. It is also the reason for the full description of the condition of certain drawings. If some of the data recorded in the Appendix has been known to specialists, it has not hitherto been set down for students of art history. A fair proportion of the drawings included have never before been exhibited.

A hundred years ago no museum in the United States possessed a work by Ingres. There was, however, a Swiss family settled in New York that had known and loved him as a friend, a family whose appearance and qualities he had recorded. Their descendants still possess three of the portrait drawings made in Florence. Mr. Roger Guerber has generously lent them to our exhibition, the only three drawings shown which still belong to the family for which they were made. They have come to join others which have traveled more widely. The first one comes to us from California where it has been since 1885 when it made the journey from Germany. Collectors and museums in the Midwest as well as the East Coast have lent drawings that they have acquired from English, Swiss and French sources.

The two notable exhibitions of Ingres' work held in Paris in 1911 and in 1934 contained not a single loan from America. The first occasion when a number of Ingres drawings were shown in the United States was the *David and Ingres* exhibition organized in 1939 by Knoedler & Co., an exhibition which was shown in four museums. Fifteen of the thirty-five drawings shown in that exhibition are included in the present one. The most recent Ingres exhibition was organized by Paul Rosenberg & Co. of New York in 1961. Twenty-nine of the seventy-three entries in that exhibition are in the present one. The interest in the work of Ingres, first apparent between the two world wars, has increased significantly since World War II.

This centennial exhibition of Ingres comes just four years after the great retrospective which marked the centennial of his arch rival, Delacroix. So different were the gifts and genius of the two great contemporaries, so diverse in kind and quantity their works, that any exhibition devoted to the work of one is, perforce, entirely different in conception and in effect from an exhibition devoted to the other. The smoke of the long and bitter battle that raged between the supporters of the Romantic and the Classic ideals has cleared, and we can now see that the lines dividing the two factions were never quite as sharp as their contemporaries had supposed. In their handling of the tools of their calling, however, Delacroix and Ingres were as different as two men could be.

The dark-haired, compact, handsome young man of twenty-four with the burning eyes, who looks out so fiercely from the self-portrait of 1804, now at Chantilly, his chalk balanced almost like a stiletto in his hand, was aptly described by his lifelong friend Delécluze. "Ingres has changed neither in physiognomy nor in manner since his adolescence. That which is true of his person is no less true of his character, which has kept a foundation of rigid honesty which never compromises with injustice or evil, and of his disposition which is always at the same level. He is one of those men who has come into the world as one pours a statue of bronze. Everything that characterizes the talent of this artist today ... was already evident in his first efforts" (E.-J. Delécluze, *Louis David, Son école et son temps,* Paris, 1855, pp. 84-85). Fifty-five years after the Chantilly painting, Ingres again portrayed himself in the *Self-Portrait* now in the Fogg. He was then seventy-nine. In the two portraits the position of the head is almost the same. The contours, less taut with the passing of time, have changed only slightly. The look is still sure, still alert, still challenging. He had a channeled ambition from the first. How steadily, how forcefully he followed the path he first had chosen at the age of nine! In his long career there were disappointments, crises, and even, if we are to follow the records of the French Academy in Rome, a series of illnesses. But from each he seems to have gathered a firmer determination, pursuing his ideal of perfection until the eve of his death at eighty-seven.

Probably the most serious and certainly, to him, the most regretted misfortune was the early break in his formal education. He was only eleven when that ended. The Revolution closed his school at Montauban, one run by the Brothers of Christian Doctrine. The endless notes in his many *cahiers* preserved at Montauban, the lengthy copying out of whole chapters from the books he had been reading, the lonely discipline of self-instruction, marked him for life. Learned though he became through his unbounded respect for knowledge and his zeal in acquiring it, he was never quite at his ease with those to whom a general cultivation in art, literature and music came naturally through more favorable circumstances. He was apt to be prickly in the presence of such men, a natural reaction, perhaps, in one so eager and so acutely aware of every nuance of intelligence and of rank. Sent away from home by his father, a modest sculptor and amateur musician who had introduced his son to the arts, Ingres entered the Academy at Toulouse at eleven to study painting and sculpture. Within two years he had won a first prize for a "rounded figure." At fourteen he was earning his own way by performing evenings as a second violinist in the orchestra of the *Capital*. Later he remembered having played a Viotti concerto when the death of Louis XVI was announced. He would have been thirteen at the time.

An early drawing, now at Montauban, after the cast of an antique sculptured head is familiar. Less well-known are the very small portrait drawings done before he went north to Paris. Three are in the present exhibition (Nos. 1, 2 and 3). These he signed *"Ingres fils,"* surely to distinguish them from the portraits by his father which are similarly small, bust-length miniatures. Yet even at sixteen or seventeen the son had qualities his father never displayed. Within the small format, there is an extraordinary vibrance of personality, a lively look about the mouths, an alertness in the eyes, an absolute control of the brief, parallel short strokes which create the collars, shoulders and cravats of the figures. In the light of his later choice of special papers, it is noteworthy that two of these early drawings are on parchment (see Technical Appendix). The eager vitality of the young artist is under complete control, governed by a sure and probing eye, and a measured judgment. Both gifts were to remain constant throughout his life, whatever the scale or the character of the figure before him.

He was seventeen when he went to Paris to enter David's flourishing, populous and noisy studio. To one of his puritanical background, puritanical in the way that only one from a mediterranean background can sometimes be, the freedom and easy ways of David's studio must have proved both a revelation and a shock. The evidence is striking. In the *Head of a Girl* (No. 4), Ingres swung briefly to an extreme contrast.

The head is the largest in scale of any that we know, the contours are bold, the drawing of the drapery remarkably quick and free, yet his love of rhythm is ever-present. In place of the parallel strokes that gave light and shade to the miniatures, he has used an almost *tachist* technique. It is one familiar to those who have seen the unfinished oil portraits by David, such as *Mme. Trudaine* (Louvre) or such portrait drawings as the *Portrait of Lepelletier de St. Fargeau* (Bibliothèque Nationale).

Having once swung widely, however, the pendulum soon found its own natural rhythm, a cadence somewhat wider than the early one, yet not as broad as that sudden, brief sweep under the impact of a totally new ambiance. His own personal, distinguished tempo, once discovered, was one to which he held steadily for the rest of his days, not in a dullness of exact repetition, but in an infinite number of subtle variations. And as time passed there was a steady growth of heart and understanding behind the observing eye and the skilled hand. Before his departure in the fall of 1806 from Paris for Rome, the familiar characteristics of his drawing style were well established, the delicate yet firm contour, the definite yet discreet distortions of form, the almost uncanny capacity to seize a likeness in the precise yet lively delineation of features.

The preferred materials were also already established: the sharply pointed graphite pencil on a smooth white paper. So familiar to us are both the materials and the manner that we forget how extraordinary they must have seemed at the time. David had used white paper and occasionally a pointed graphite pencil, but never with such constancy, such subtlety or such harmony. Flaxman had loved a finely delineated clean contour, but had never achieved a comparable variety or tensile strength of line. Ingres' manner of drawing was as new as the century. It was immediately recognized as expert and admirable. If his paintings were sternly criticized as "Gothic," no comparable criticism was leveled at his drawings. It is also fascinating to note that, although the Napoleonic Wars were shaking Europe, Ingres was able to obtain in his early years in Rome, English papers of the finest quality, papers with a smooth, even surface that recorded the slightest touch of his graphite point.

His astonishing capacity to record a likeness was quickly known. At twenty-three he had been commissioned to paint the portrait of the First Consul. Napoleon liked it so much that when he became Emperor, Ingres was commissioned to do another. The second is no warmer than the first; clearly, the official *portrait d'apparat* was never to engage the artist's deepest commitment. What was true of the painted portrait was even more true of the portrait drawings. One has only to turn these pages to know which sitters appealed to the artist, which bored him. He did not, perhaps he could not, mask his feelings. He gives us an astonishingly vivid and sympathetic picture of his Roman milieu, the artists whose likes and dislikes he shared, the architects who were his companions at the Academy, the director of the Academy, the director's wife and children, the discreet and lovely wife of the merchant from whom he bought his paper, pencils, color and brushes, the proud, even cocky, officials who ruled Napoleonic Rome, and the subjects from Roman antiquity which both artist and Napoleonic patron considered suitable for the enlightened conquerors, *Romulus Victorious over Acron, Virgil Reading the "Aeneid,"* the *Dream of Ossian.*

The early years in Italy were the only ones, with one or two exceptions, when he turned his eye and hand to landscape. The light of Rome may have been the main force which moved him to record for his fiancée the surroundings in which he was living, but we would like to suggest another source which may have given him a certain impetus.

In the early winter of 1806-1807, Pierre-Adrien Pâris (1745-1819) returned to Rome "to warm his old bones" in southern sunlight. Pâris, an architect, draughtsman and collector, had lived in Rome from 1771-1774. Joseph-Benoit Suvée (1743-1807) had been a *prix de Rome* at the same time. The two became and remained friends. In the autumn of 1806, Suvée invited his old friend to visit him at the French Academy of which he was then Director. Through Suvée's initiative it had been moved from the Palazzo Mangani in the Corso up to the Villa Medici. Suddenly, in January, 1807, Suvée died of a stroke of apoplexy while talking to some students. Alquier, the French Ambassador in Rome, acting quickly and, as it turned out, very wisely, urged Pâris to step in and become the interim Director until a new man could be chosen and make the journey to Rome.

Because of the Napoleonic successes, the school was larger than it had ever been. There were twenty *pensionnaires*. It needed an experienced guiding hand and a man of firm judgment. Pâris accepted the charge. He served from January to October, when Guillon Lethière arrived to assume the post.

Pâris, in his final report, 2 October 1807, the last of several illuminating and admirable documents which record his wise administration, recommended to the French authorities that instead of sending musicians to Rome, he would favor the appointment to the school of landscape painters. "This countryside is extremely rich in varied and attractive sites. The climate gives to the color a vigor and a brightness of which those in northern climates have no conception, while the air has soft mists which produce decided effects in aerial perspective. Intermingled with the buildings and the majestic ruins are the most lovely, spontaneous growths of nature. Together they compose landscapes of the grandest and most noble style. Where else but in Rome and its surroundings could Claude Lorrain, Poussin, Gaspar Poussin and Salvator Rosa have been formed?" (Lapauze, 1924, II, p. 78, translation, the writer's.) Pâris, conscious of the change of taste, as well as of sovereigns, diplomatically refers to the paintings of the seventeenth century. One remembers, however, his princely bequest to his native Besançon of the innumerable magnificent landscape drawings which Hubert Robert and Fragonard had made in Rome. Pâris' description fits them as well as it does the work of the earlier masters.

The youthful Ingres, new to Rome, could hardly have been indifferent to the passionate and perceptive enthusiasms of such a man, especially when shortly after Ingres' arrival that man was running the school at the Villa Medici. Surely Pâris' shadow stands behind Ingres as he essays in 1807, for the first and last time, some painted views of Rome, and turns his hand to a series of landscape drawings of great purity, economy and sensitivity.

After 1815, the Bonaparte dream faded quickly. The Empire was lost and Rome with it, but not before Ingres had found Lucien (No. 11), a more sympathetic sitter than his brother, and Lucien's devoted family, a group of beguiling and engrossing interest (No. 33). How he charmed them into stillness long enough to assess their temperaments and record their delicate finery will be forever a mystery.

Their fall from power left the artist without patrons and, in some cases, without payment. Grudgingly, the painter of history had to gain a thin livelihood drawing the portraits of the new French residents, now the nation's representatives at the Vatican, and the visiting British. The latter, released from the confines of their island when the Napoleonic Wars were over, flocked to Rome for diversion and enlightenment.

The quality of the Restoration French can be gauged in the contrast they make to their immediate predecessors. Mallet, the Napoleonic army engineer (No. 14) is full of swagger, conscious of his competence and power. The Jordans and their children are of quite a different stripe, aristocrats with roots in the *ancien régime,* cultivated, elegant, assured (Nos. 40-41). For them Ingres uses a larger format than for the visiting British, one he reserved for his good

Florentine patrons, the LeBlancs, and for the pair we here identify as the Austrian minister and his fashionable and beautiful wife (Nos. 55-56).

Ingres fussed about his English clients. He turned firmly from his door the one who had the indiscretion to ask, when the artist answered his knock, if the portrait draughtsman lived there. "Non, Monsieur," was the response as he turned the inquirer away, "a painter of history lives here." Yet he must have found the visiting British fascinating. The liveliness, the justness and the penetration of their portraits belie his cry of boredom.

"Il ne faut pas essayer d'apprendre à faire le beau caractère," he later told his students, "il faut le trouver dans le modèle." In his portraits he himself had looked so sharply and estimated so justly every shade of distinction—moral, social and national—and every facet of character that we need the documentary data of their lives only for confirmation. With a single look we can distinguish the English nobleman, the French aristocrat, the German of ambassadorial rank; the bourgeois, the artist, the scholar; the hard taskmaster, the generous spirit, the astute politician.

Within the restricted space of a simple white page there is the infinite variety of life itself. Sometimes it is not even a face that tells the story, only a single isolated hand; yet that hand has the whole character of a man. There, in essence, in the studies of four hands is the power and force of the great newspaperman, Bertin (No. 68), the easy capability and adroitness of the almost bored public servant, Comte Molé (Nos. 74 and 75), and the elegant grace and strength of the assured aristocrat, the Duc d'Orléans (No. 84).

Portrait drawings and studies for painted portraits outnumber other studies in the present exhibition almost three to one. There is a very simple reason for this. Ingres was a firm believer in tradition in artistic standards as well as in personal behavior. Like the artists of earlier centuries, he kept the contents of his studio together, a vast mass of reference material for himself and his students. He had sold finished portrait drawings only to those sitters for whom they had been made during those years when he was under financial stress. The quick portraits of colleagues he had offered as gifts. The contents of his studio, drawings, oil sketches, paintings, books and musical scores, he bequeathed to his native town, Montauban, removing in that one gesture a vast richness from a potential market.

There was a single exception. At the very end of his life, a scant three months before his death, he was persuaded by Haro, who had been for years and years his friend as well as his supplier of canvas, paint and tools, to part with a few drawings, mostly studies for now famous paintings. Ingres agreed, no doubt out of a desire to leave his wife in somewhat better circumstances. Many of the figure drawings in the present exhibition (Nos. 21, 25, 57, 68, 74, 75, 84, 87, 103 and 106) are now in America because of that decision.

A moving example of his respect for traditional behavior was his rigid refusal to put himself forward as a candidate for the Institute when a place became vacant in 1824. He felt that Charles Thévenin, who had been director at Rome after Lethière and who was a friend, should take precedence over him, even though his heart cried out for the honor as he confessed in a letter to his wife. He actively supported Thévenin's candidacy and Thévenin received the place. Fate stepped in to redress the balance a year later. At the unexpected death in 1825 of his old enemy, Denon, Ingres was able to offer his candidacy. This time he was immediately successful.

His love of family and his devotion to his friends form a *leitmotif* throughout his work. A true friend once found became a friend forever, and the friends' friends were accepted as well. Their names occur and recur. We meet them in Rome in 1809, '10 and '11, in Florence in the early twenties, and then later again in Rome and in Paris. We follow their marriages, their careers, their children and children's children. Childless himself, he records with piercing poignancy the enchanting children of his friends.

As he grows older, the hard point sometimes is replaced by a softer one, a light brown paper occasionally supplants the white, and white highlights are added to the graphite. The forms become a little fuller, the interpretation a little warmer. The circle in which he moves, now that he himself is almost a *monument historique,* is more ample in outlook as well as in form.

The drawings for the great early schemes, for the *Acron* and for the *Virgil,* proclaim his devotion to antiquity and to his divinity, Raphael. In fact, the difference between these early studies and his later figure drawings, such as those for the *Golden Age* (No. 67), reflects a development similar to the evolution of Raphael's draughtsmanship. Just as Raphael's drawings made in Rome ca. 1518 possess an ease, a breadth of vision and a largeness of design which were not present in the Florentine drawings of 1504, analogous changes have occurred in Ingres' work, changes that come with wisdom and practice. Ingres' drawings can support the comparison to one of the very greatest of draughtsmen, although his rate of growth was, of course, much slower.

This exhibition of drawings, watercolors and oil sketches takes us into the inner core of the artist's life. To the outer world he occasionally appeared cantankerous, blindly partisan and severely limited. One of his oft-repeated maxims was the ancient one: to know oneself. He knew himself profoundly. Many contemporaries saw his faults and interpreted his habit of returning to a subject to try to better it as evidence of a lack of imaginative gifts. They could not have carefully counted the number of subjects he essayed in one medium or another. They found his pronouncements tiresome.

They underestimated both his intellect and his genius. His concentration encompassed more than was immediately visible. A single instance can serve for many. The two figures of the *Iliad* and the *Odyssey,* who sit at the feet of Homer in the *Apotheosis of Homer* were studied again and again in a number of different drawings as he searched to find the form and pose that would best sustain his inner meaning. Finally he was ready, and he wrote a friend his intention. "At the foot of Homer is the Iliad (No. 57) with a proud and martial air, holding her two knees close in her two hands. Her clothes, her hair slightly in disorder, recall at the same time Achilles hiding in the clothing of the young girls of Lycomede and Achilles, irritated, retired to his tent. The Odyssey entirely enveloped with a sea green drapery, an oar at her side, a souvenir of perilous voyages, observes, meditates: it is Ulysses." (Quoted by Eugène Montrosier,

*Peintres Modernes,* Paris, 1882, pp. 32-35.) One does not need the interpretation to value the strength, beauty and majesty of the figure. But because the meaning is there, thoroughly present to the artist who brought the figure into being, we too become aware, perhaps without knowing it, of deep significance in the form he represents.

To many of his students, Ingres was such a powerful force that he seems to have drained them of all personality. His true followers were those of such strong gifts of their own that they could profit from his stern examples: Degas, for example, who worshipped him and collected his work; Renoir, who watched quietly from a distance with fascinated admiration as Ingres made quick drawings in the Bibliothèque Nationale and who subjected himself for a period to an Ingresque discipline of line; and Picasso who has turned to Ingres again and again, both overtly and covertly.

If the savants of the *Gazette* saw clearly, their views were not always shared by their contemporaries. Montrosier, for example, found that although Ingres had evoked the past, interrogated Raphael, and removed the dust from some tombs, he had taught his contemporaries nothing and built nothing to instruct his descendants. "His glory is precarious; it will not last. Posterity alone will confirm our words." Posterity has taken a different view, as so often happens. To Ingres' twentieth-century descendants, he is, especially in his drawings, a continuing source of instruction, illumination, science and pure delight.

AGNES MONGAN

14 *January* 1967

# ANNOTATED CHRONOLOGY *

### I. 1780-97: EARLY LIFE IN MONTAUBAN AND STUDY IN TOULOUSE

Earliest study with his father, a draughtsman, painter, sculptor, amateur musician, known as "le bon ornemaniste toulousain." Observes father's work in decorative complexes and miniature portraits. Age 11, sent by father to study figure painting, landscape painting, and sculpture at the Academy of Toulouse. Recognized for skill in rendering bodily forms. Does medallion portrait drawings.

| | |
|---|---|
| 29 August 1780 | Jean-Auguste-Dominique Ingres born in Montauban, first of five children of Toulouse-born Jean-Marie-Joseph Ingres (1755-1814) and Montalbanaise Anne Moulet. |
| 1786-90 | Formal academic education with the Brothers of the Christian Doctrine. Studies drawing and music with father. |
| 1789 | First known drawing, head after antique cast, signed and dated later. |
| 1791-97 | Studies at the Academy of Toulouse with painter Guillaume-Joseph Roques, sculptor de Vigan, and landscape painter Jean Briant. Studies violin with Lejeune, and from ages 13-16 is second violinist in Capital Orchestra. Between 1792-97, wins prizes in "composition," "figure and antique," "rounded figure," and "life studies." |

### II. 1797-1806: FIRST PERIOD IN PARIS

Goes to Paris to study with David. Enters his atelier. Develops his own personal style in reaction to David's "icy style." Influenced by the pure contour of Etruscan painting, the Paris group known as the *Primitifs,* the English sculptor-illustrator John Flaxman, and Raphael. Wins *Prix de Rome* in 1801. Acclaimed by Flaxman. Remains in Paris, forced to wait for travel funds until 1806. Paints in variety of genres: torso studies, history paintings, and numerous portraits (including official portraits). Experiments in his color, using tonal relations rather than contrasting hues. Between 1801-05, has atelier in ex-Capuchin Monastery where he is closely associated with Italian sculptor L. Bartolini and Belgium music theorist F.-J. Fétis. Championed by friends Gérard, Forbin, Granger and C. Vernet.

| | |
|---|---|
| August, 1797 | With son of Roques, leaves Montauban for Paris, to enter David's atelier. |
| 24 October 1799 | Forty-fourth out of eighty-eight candidates competing for entrance into the Painting Department, École des Beaux-Arts. |
| 2 February 1800 | First prize in half-figure "torso" painting. |
| 30 March 1800 | Second prize, preliminary try, *Prix de Rome,* for his *Cincinnatus.* |
| 4 October 1800 | Second grand prize, for his *Antiochus and Scipio.* |
| 20 March 1801 | Second class, trial contest, *Prix de Rome,* for his *Hector and Andromache.* |
| 29 September 1801 | First *Grand Prix de Rome* with *The Envoys from Agamemnon.* |
| 17 December 1801 | Named associate correspondent of the Society of Sciences and Arts of Montauban. |
| 2 September 1802 | Exhibits for first time in Salon with portrait of a woman. |

* Largely based upon Georges Wildenstein, *The Paintings of J. A. D. Ingres,* London, 1954, pp. 21-29.

| 17 July 1803 | Commissioned to paint *Portrait of First Consul* for the city of Liège. |
| June, 1806 | Engaged to Anne-Marie-Julie Forestier. |
| 15 September 1806 | Salon Musée Napoleon; exhibits *Napoleon I on Imperial Throne, Self-Portrait,* and portraits of *M., Mme., and Mlle. Rivière.* Critics harsh; Chaussard criticizes him for being "gothic," "barbaric," "vulgar" and "dry." |

## III.   1806-20: First Period in Rome

Style develops under influences of Etruscan painting, Flaxman's engraved illustrations of classical sources, 15th- and 16th-century Italian painting (Masaccio, Fra Angelico, Raphael, Titian), and 17th-century French neo-classicism (Poussin). Copies these masters' works. Very productive years. Painting portraits, subjects from history, mythology, the theatre, religious tradition. Introduces compositions and themes which he will rework and duplicate throughout his career (e.g. *The Bather, Odalisque, Antiochus and Stratonice*). Talent for capturing traits of personality and physiognomy. Numerous pencil portraits of foreign visitors and officials; begins to use softer graphite, occasionally combining hard with soft points to get tonal effects. Paints landscapes, copies old masters, and paints history subjects in watercolor. Ca. 1810, beginning of lifelong friendships with the engraver Gatteaux and the *functionnaire* M. Marcotte d'Argenteuil.

| 11 October 1806 | Arrives in Rome. |
| 26 December 1806-<br>November, 1810 | *Pensionnaire* at the Villa Medici, the French Academy in Rome. Has studio in San Gaetano on the Pincio. |
| 2 July 1807 | Breaks engagement with Julie Forestier. |
| 1810 | Moves to no. 40, via Gregoriana. |
| 1811 | Exhibits *Jupiter and Thetis* at Académie des Beaux-Arts, Paris. |
| 11 December 1812 | Becomes engaged to a Dane, Laure Zoëga. Brief engagement is broken. |
| 4 December 1813 | Marries Madeleine Chapelle (1782-1849) at San Martino ai Monti, Rome. |
| 14 March 1814 | Father dies in Montauban. |
| Spring 1814 | Visits Naples. Paints Queen Caroline Murat and royal family (painting lost). |
| 1 November 1814 | Salon of 1814, Paris, exhibits *Don Pedro of Toledo, Raphael and the Fornarina* (Fogg), *Interior View of Sistine Chapel,* and several portraits. Most critics unkind. Still praised by Flaxman. |
| 1815 | Downfall of Napoleon's dynasty and empire. Mme. Ingres' child is stillborn. |
| 14 March 1817 | Ingres' mother dies in Montauban. |
| 1817 | *Christ Giving the Keys of Heaven to Saint Peter* commissioned for Trinità dei Monti. |
| June, 1819 | Visits sculptor L. Bartolini in Florence. |
| 25 August 1819 | Salon of 1819, Paris, exhibits *Grand Odalisque, Philip V and the Marshall of Berwick, Roger and Angelica.* Receives sarcastic criticism. His *Odalisque* is called "gothic." |

## IV.   1820-24: Florentine Period

Lives at first with family of friend Bartolini. Fascinated by Renaissance painting and history. Copies Raphael, Titian, Andrea del Sarto. Continues remunerative pencil portraits. Spends evenings either at the theatre or playing and listening to music. Eventually resides at no. 6550 via della Colonna and has studio at via delle Belle Donne. Main work of period is the Raphaelesque *Vow of Louis XIII* (1820-24), ordered for the Cathedral of Montauban.

| | |
|---|---|
| 22 December 1823 | Honored with election as corresponding member of Académie des Beaux-Arts. |
| 25 August 1824 | Salon of 1824, Paris, exhibits *Henry IV with his Children, Death of Leonardo, Sistine Chapel, Dauphin's Entry into Paris,* Aretino series, and several portraits. |

## V.   1824-34: Second Paris Period

Encouraged to return to Paris after his work is enthusiastically received in the *salon* of 1824. Concentrates on history painting, working on two familiar themes (*Apotheosis of Homer* and *Martyrdom of St. Symphorien*). Few painted portraits in addition to the well-known *M. Bertin.* Continues making portraits in graphite for friends. Resides with friend Charles Thévenin, then 4 rue de Bourbon, 49 quai des Grands Augustins, and passage Sainte-Marie on the rue du Bac, with studios for himself and students on rue des Marais, Saint Germain.

| | |
|---|---|
| October, 1824 | Arrives in Paris. |
| 12 November 1824 | Salon of 1824, Paris, exhibits *Vow of Louis XIII,* brought with him from Florence. Generally well received. Marie-Henri Beyle (Stendhal) claims *Vow* lacks feeling, lacks "the impression of divinity." |
| Early 1825 | Receives Cross of Legion of Honor from Charles X. |
| 25 June 1825 | Elected a member of the Académie des Beaux-Arts, replacing the late Baron Vivant-Denon. |
| November, 1825 | Visits Autun, draws porte Saint-André and Roman enclosure walls for *Martyrdom of St. Symphorien.* |
| 1826 | *Apotheosis of Homer* commissioned. |
| 1827 | Becomes resident at the Institute. |
| 4 November 1827 | Salon of 1827, Paris. Hangs *Apotheosis of Homer* in the Louvre. Exhibits *Comte de Pastoret, Mme. Marcotte de Sainte Marie, Oedipus and the Sphinx* in the Salon. Reviews are favorable. |
| 30 December 1829 | Named Professor at École des Beaux-Arts, replacing Jean-Baptiste Regnault. |
| 31 July 1830 | Revolution. Joins Delacroix and others in protecting the Louvre paintings, specifically the Italian School. |
| 1833-34 | Serves as Vice-President and then President of École des Beaux-Arts. |
| 1 March 1833 | Exhibits *Bertin the Elder, Mme. Devauçay* in the Salon. |
| 1 May 1833 | Receives the cross of Officer of the Legion of Honor. |
| 1834 | Exhibits *Martyrdom of St. Symphorien* and *Mme. Leblanc* in the Salon. Public reaction is reserved. |

## VI.   1834-41: Second Period in Rome

Directorship of the French Academy in Rome. Concentrates on theory and on teaching. Revises curriculum of Academy, founding an archaeology course and adding more life classes. Also adds a library and antique and renaissance casts to the galleries. Number of extant works suggests this is his least productive period. Paints religious subjects, portraits and Odalisque. Draws portrait of

Poussin for printed illustration in first edition, *le Plutarque Français* (Paris, 1836). Attracted to color and patterns found in Mogul painting. Surrounds himself with musician friends, Cherubini and Gounod among them.

| December, 1834 | Travels to Rome via cities of northern and central Italy with wife and a student, Georges Lefrançois. |
| 1835-41 | Director of the French Academy in Rome. |
| 1835-36 | Cholera epidemic. Ingres considers it his duty to be on hand, so stays at the Academy. |
| 1840 | Completes *Odalisque with Slave, Virgin with the Host, Antiochus and Stratonice* (Chantilly). |

## VII.  1841-67: Third and Final Period in Paris

Château de Dampierre commission of the '40s never finished. Depressed by death in 1849 of first wife, Madeleine. In 1852 friends induce him to remarry. Second marriage seems to rejuvenate him. Accelerated activity. Revives the familiar subjects of his history paintings, religious themes, and the bather. Paints eight outstandingly successful female portraits. Draws portraits of Le Sueur, Molière, La Fontaine, Racine for second edition of *Plutarque Français* (Paris, 1844-47). Concerned with modern subjects as evidenced by his notes (*Cahier IX*). Pencil portraits made with softer graphite, freer line, and more robust modeling. Paints in watercolors for clients, wife and friends. In his 80's, Ingres still hopes to learn by copying a Holbein portrait. His last work is a tracing after a photograph of a Giotto.

| Spring 1841 | After travel through Tuscany, revisits Bartolini and returns to Paris. Upon return, celebrated and honored by concert organized by Berlioz. Entertained by Louis-Philippe. Given seat reserved for life membership in Théâtre de Comédie Français. |
| May, 1842 | Finishes portrait of the late *Duc d'Orléans*. |
| June, 1842 | Receives Prussian Cross of Civil Merit. |
| August, 1843-November, 1849 | Lives and works at Château de Dampierre for Duc de Luynes. Works on two wall decorations, the *Golden Age* (unfinished) and the *Iron Age* (only sketched). Abandons project after death of wife. |
| 24 August 1845 | Named commander of Legion of Honor. |
| 11 January 1846 | Exhibits eleven paintings (including portraits of *Comte Molé and Comtesse d'Haussonville*, and *Odalisque with Slave* (Fogg) in Benefit Exhibition for Pension and Aid Fund, Société des Artistes, Galérie des Beaux-Arts. |
| June, 1848 | Refuses to be candidate for Constituent Assembly. |
| 29 October 1848 | As member of the Commission of Fine Arts, seeks freedom of admission to the Salon and suppression of the Jury. |
| 1849-50 | Again Vice-President (1849) and President (1850) of École des Beaux-Arts. |
| June-July, 1849 | Travels in Jersey, Avranches, Bayeaux, Caen. |
| 27 July 1849 | Death of Mme. Madeleine Ingres. |
| 1851 | Albert Magimel publishes *Oeuvres de J.-A.-D. Ingres, 1800-51*. |
| 18 July 1851 | Presents fifty-one paintings to the City of Montauban, the first donation of work to his native town. |

| | |
|---|---|
| 25 October 1851 | Terminates service of twenty-eight years and resigns as professor of the École des Beaux-Arts. |
| 15 April 1852 | Second marriage. Seventy-one-year-old Ingres marries forty-three-year-old relative of Marcotte, Mlle. Delphine Ramel (1808-87). |
| 2 March 1853 | *The Apotheosis of Napoleon I,* ceiling decoration commissioned for Emperor's Salon, Hôtel de Ville. |
| 19 August 1853 | With in-laws and Mme. Guille, buys summer home in Meung-sur-Loire where thirteen summers are enjoyed. |
| February, 1854 | Emperor and Empress visit Ingres' Paris studio. |
| 15 May 1854 | Inauguration of the Ingres room in the Montauban Hôtel de Ville, now Musée Ingres. |
| 15 May-<br>15 November 1854 | Shows forty-three paintings, including *Princesse de Broglie, Cherubini and Muse, Mme. Reiset, Mme. Moitessier,* 1851, *Jupiter and Antiope, Mme. Henri Gonse,* and twenty-five stained glass cartoons at Exposition Universelle. Decorated Grand Officer of the Legion of Honor by the Emperor. Baudelaire praises Ingres for portraiture but criticizes him for lack of "imagination" and movement. |
| September, 1855 | Visits the Edme Ramels in Cannes. |
| 1858 | Sends *Self-Portrait* to Museum of Florence. |
| 1861 | In early months of this year friends organize exhibition of ninety-two drawings by Ingres, held at Salon des Arts-Unis, Paris. |
| 1862 | International Exhibition, London. Exhibits the *Source* (1856). |
| April, 1862 | Exposition des Beaux-Arts, Montauban, includes twenty-three paintings and eighteen drawings by Ingres. Exhibited *Self-Portrait* (Fogg). |
| 25 May 1862 | Named senator. |
| 4 July 1862 | Member of the Imperial Council of Public Instruction. |
| 14 July 1863 | Presented the Golden Crown; subscription arranged by student Armand Cambon. |
| November, 1863 | Protests loss of rights of Académie des Beaux-Arts over École des Beaux-Arts. |
| 3 July 1863 | Named member of Royal Fine Arts Academy, Antwerp. Sends them *Self-Portrait,* age 85. |
| 8 January 1867 | Tracing of *Christ at the Tomb,* after Giotto. |
| 14 January 1867 | Dies of double pneumonia, at 11, quai Voltaire, Paris. |
| 17 January 1867 | Funeral at Church of St. Thomas Aquinas. Buried at Père-Lachaise. Ingres' will (28 January 1866) includes bequest of his paintings and drawings (more than 4,000 of the latter), print collection, books, collection of antique sculpture, and musical possessions, to the City of Montauban. Different bequests made to his wife, friends and students. |
| Spring 1867 | Posthumous exhibition of 584 paintings, drawings, and sketches by Ingres at the École des Beaux-Arts. |

# THE CATALOGUE

BY

AGNES MONGAN AND HANS NAEF

# COMPILERS' NOTE

WHENEVER POSSIBLE, the catalogue reproductions were made directly from the originals. Only 29 of the 116 illustrations are based upon photographs. An asterisk following the measurements of a drawing, watercolor or oil sketch indicates that the reproduction is the same size as the work of art. This is true of 37 entries. Actual size details of two major group portraits (Nos. 5 and 33) have also been included.

Reproductions of paintings associated with the exhibition's numerous preparatory studies have been included in the Photographic Supplement at the back of the catalogue. Cross references to specific entries are noted in each caption.

Whenever it proved possible, drawings were removed from their frames, remeasured and critically examined (see Technical Appendix). Significant changes which are visible to the naked eye, either reworking by the artist or later damage, are discussed under the heading "Condition." Explanations of an object's technical history and current appearance are offered only if written records exist or if it has been possible to study the drawing under laboratory conditions.

We omitted all references to exhibitions unaccompanied by a catalogue of interest to scholars. Lugt numbers are cited only when a collector's mark actually appears on the drawing. Fogg accession numbers are recorded at the close of our entries.

The following bibliographical abbreviations have been used:

| | |
|---|---|
| Paris, 1861 | Paris, Salon des Arts-Unis, 1861, *Dessins (d'Ingres) tirés de collections d'amateurs.* |
| Galichon, 1861 | Émile Galichon, "Description des dessins de M. Ingres exposés au Salon des Arts-Unis," *Gazette des Beaux-Arts,* IX, March, 1861, pp. 343 ff. |
| Paris, 1867 | Paris, École impériale des beaux-arts, 1867, *Tableaux, études peintes, dessins et croquis de J.-A.-D. Ingres.* |
| Blanc, 1870 | Charles Blanc, *Ingres, sa vie et ses ouvrages,* Paris, 1870. |
| Delaborde, 1870 | Henri Delaborde, *Ingres, sa vie, ses travaux, sa doctrine,* Paris, 1870. |
| Gatteaux | Édouard Gatteaux, *Collection de 120 dessins, croquis et peintures de M. Ingres,* Paris, n.d. (1875), 2 volumes. |
| Jouin, 1888 | Henry Jouin, *Musée de portraits d'artistes,* Paris, 1888. |
| Lapauze, 1901 | Henry Lapauze, *Les Dessins de J. A. D. Ingres du Musée de Montauban,* Paris, 1901. |
| Lapauze, 1903 | Henry Lapauze, *Les Portraits dessinés de J. A. D. Ingres,* Paris, 1903. |
| Thieme-Becker | Dr. Ulrich Thieme and Dr. Felix Becker, *Allgemeines Lexikon der Bildenden Künstler,* Leipzig, 1907-50. |
| Lapauze, 1910 | Henry Lapauze, *Le Roman d'amour de M. Ingres,* Paris, 1910. |
| Lapauze, 1911 | Henry Lapauze, *Ingres, sa vie et son oeuvre,* Paris, 1911. |
| Lapauze, *Briant,* 1911 | Henry Lapauze, *Jean Briant paysagiste, maître de Ingres, et le paysage dans l'oeuvre de Ingres,* Paris, 1911. |
| Paris, 1911 | Paris, Georges Petit Galleries, 1911, *Exposition Ingres.* |
| Paris, 1921 | Paris, Chambre syndicale de la curiosité et des Beaux-Arts, 1921, *Exposition Ingres.* |
| Exposition, 1921 | *La Renaissance de l'art français et des industries de Luxe,* Special issue dedicated to *l'Exposition Ingres,* IV, No. 5, May, 1921. |

| | |
|---|---|
| L. | Fritz Lugt, *Les Marques de collections de dessins et d'estampes,* Amsterdam, 1921; Supplement, 1956. |
| Cambridge, 1929 | Cambridge, Fogg Art Museum, 1929, *Exhibition of French Painting of the Nineteenth and Twentieth Centuries.* |
| Lapauze, 1929 | Collection de M. Henry Lapauze, Sale, Paris, Hôtel Drouot, 21 June 1929. |
| Zabel, 1930 | Morton D. Zabel, "Ingres in America," *The Arts,* xvi, February, 1930, pp. 369 ff. |
| Paris, 1934 | Paris, Jacques Seligmann et fils, 1934, *Exposition de Portraits par Ingres et ses élèves.* |
| Miller, 1938 | Alexandrine Miller, "Ingres' Three Methods of Drawing as Revealed by his Crayon Portraits," *Art in America,* xxvi, January, 1938, pp. 3 ff. |
| Ford, 1939 | Brinsley Ford, "Ingres Portrait Drawings of English People at Rome, 1806-20," *Burlington Magazine,* lxxv, July, 1939, pp. 4 ff. |
| Springfield, etc., 1939-40 | Springfield, Springfield Museum of Fine Arts, New York, Knoedler, Cincinnati, Cincinnati Art Museum, and Rochester, Rochester Memorial Art Museum, 1939-40, *David and Ingres, Paintings and Drawings.* |
| Mongan-Sachs, 1940 | Agnes Mongan and Paul J. Sachs, *Drawings in the Fogg Museum of Art,* Cambridge, 1940, 2 vols. |
| Mongan, 1944 | Agnes Mongan, "Drawings by Ingres in the Winthrop Collection," *Gazette des Beaux-Arts,* xxvi, July-December, 1944, pp. 387 ff. |
| Mongan, 1947 | Agnes Mongan, *Ingres, Twenty-four Drawings,* New York, Pantheon, 1947. |
| San Francisco, 1947 | San Francisco, Palace of the Legion of Honor, 1947, *Nineteenth-Century French Drawings.* |
| Alazard, 1950 | Jean Alazard, *Ingres et l'Ingrisme,* Paris, 1950. |
| Shoolman-Slatkin, 1950 | Regina Shoolman and Charles E. Slatkin, *Six Centuries of French Master Drawings in America,* New York, 1950. |
| Wildenstein, 1954 | Georges Wildenstein, *The Paintings of J. A. D. Ingres,* London, 1954. |
| Schlenoff, 1956 | Norman Schlenoff, *Ingres, ses sources littéraires,* Paris, 1956. |
| Zurich and Rome, 1958 | Zurich, Kunsthaus Zurich, and Rome, Palazzo Braschi, 1958, *Rome vue par Ingres.* |
| Rotterdam, Paris, New York, 1958-59 | Rotterdam, Boymans Museum, Paris, Musée de l'Orangerie, New York, Museum of Modern Art, 1958-59, *French Drawings from American Collections, Clouet to Matisse.* Editions of the catalogue were published in Rotterdam, Paris and New York. Our references are to the French edition since the Dutch and English ones are out of print. |
| Ternois, 1959 | Daniel Ternois, *Les Dessins d'Ingres au Musée de Montauban, Les Portraits* (Inventaire général des dessins des musées de province, iii), Paris, 1959. |
| Naef, 1960 | Hans Naef, *Rome vue par Ingres,* Lausanne, 1960. |
| New York, 1961 | New York, Paul Rosenberg & Co., 1961, *Ingres in American Collections.* |
| Mongan, 1962 | Ira Moskowitz (ed.), *Great Drawings of All Time,* New York, 1962, iii, French, text by A. Mongan. |
| Naef, 1963 | Hans Naef, "Ingres und die Familie Guillon Lethière," *Du,* xxiii, December, 1963, pp. 65 ff. |
| Naef, 1967 | Hans Naef, "Eighteen Portrait Drawings by Ingres," *Master Drawings,* iv, No. 3, to be published. |

# ACKNOWLEDGMENTS

WE have been generously assisted in every phase by Mary Lee Bennett.

We are grateful to Mary Beebe, Carol Collins Gillham, Phyllis Hattis, Eliza Mason, John Rhodes, Patricia Durand Rumsey, Jane Strumsky, Eunice Williams and Dorothy Usher Wilson of the Drawing Department, to Marjorie Benedict Cohn and Steven Herbert of the Conservation Department, to H. Wade White, Archivist, to Catherine Scott Coté, Michael Nedzweski and James Ufford of the Photography Department, to Elisabeth Strassmann, Registrar, and her assistant, Elizabeth Hoover, to Peter A. Wick, Assistant Director, and to Milton Worthley, all of the Fogg Art Museum, and to William Bond, Philip Hofer and Helen D. Willard of the Houghton Library. We also wish to thank Louise Guerber Burroughs, David Daniels, Elizabeth Mongan and the directors and curatorial staffs of the lending institutions for their assistance, especially Jacob Bean, Claus Virch, Margaretta Salinger and Linda Boyer of the Metropolitan Museum of Art, Olive Bragazzi, New York, Charles Chetham of the Smith College Museum of Art, Frederick J. Cummings and Ellen Sharp of the Detroit Institute of Arts, Henry S. Francis of the Cleveland Museum of Art, Egbert Haverkamp-Begemann of the Yale University Art Gallery, Stephen B. Jareckie of the Worcester Art Museum, Harold Joachim of the Art Institute of Chicago, Thomas W. Leavitt of the Santa Barbara Museum of Art, Stephen E. Ostrow of the Art Association of Indianapolis, Emily S. Rauh of the City Art Museum of St. Louis, Eleanor A. Sayre and Anne B. Smith of the Museum of Fine Arts, Boston, Alan Shestack of the National Gallery of Art, and George Szabo of the Lehman Collection. Our French colleagues have been of great help, particularly Wanda Bouleau-Rabaud of the École des Beaux-Arts, André Grellou of the Musée Ingres, Edouard Morot-Sir, Cultural Counselor attached to the French Embassy, New York, Maurice Sérullaz of the Louvre, Daniel Ternois of the University of Lyons, and Liliane O. Ziegel, Paris. We are also grateful to Robert M. Light, Lucien Goldschmidt, M. Roy Fisher of Wildenstein and Company, Helmut Ripperger of M. Knoedler and Company, Alexandre Rosenberg of Paul Rosenberg and Company, Germain Seligman of Jacques Seligmann and Company, and to Mr. and Mrs. Charles E. Slatkin. Last but not least, we are deeply indebted to our patient and resourceful friends, Harold Hugo, John Peckham, William J. Glick, Roger Bartlett, and Frank Poll of The Meriden Gravure Company and to Warren F. Skillings of The Anthoensen Press.

Dr. Hans Naef's stay in Cambridge was made possible by a special grant through the University, supplemented by the Julius Adams Stratton Prize for Cultural Achievement, the latter awarded for the first time by the American Society for Friendship with Switzerland, Boston Chapter.

Graphite with black and gray gouache on cream-colored paper. Diameter, 3¾ in. (95 mm.)*

Signed near the lower right edge: *Ingres fils.*

PROVENANCE:     Acquired by Judge Edwin B. Crocker in Germany, ca. 1871; bequeathed by his widow, Margaret E. (Rhodes) Crocker, to the City of Sacramento, 1885.

In a forthcoming article, Dr. Naef will discuss a related drawing inscribed "Monsieur Brochard habile interprête de Molière" which is known to have been sold at the Hôtel Drouot, Paris, 6 June 1883. According to Max Fuches, *Lexique des troupes des Comédiens au XVIIIème siècle,* Paris, 1944, p. 281, there were actors of the name Brochard performing in Toulouse at the end of the eighteenth century. The striking resemblance between "Monsieur Brochard," dressed *en civil* rather than in costume, and the "Warrior" from the Crocker Collection suggests a possible identification for the latter, an identification which may throw new light on the whole question of the early Ingres medallion portraits.

The drawing seems to have been made at Toulouse just before Ingres left for Paris. The handwriting of the inscription is still distinctly eighteenth century in character; and, as far as we know, Ingres did not sign himself "Ingres fils" after his arrival in Paris. Even at this early date, Ingres is making his shadows in small parallel strokes which show an astonishing control. Such strokes, which grow in subtlety and refinement, are one of the main features of his later portrait drawing.

*E. B. Crocker Art Gallery, Sacramento, California*

Graphite on parchment which has been completely affixed to white laid paper. Diameter: 2$\frac{11}{16}$ in. (69 mm.)*

Signed, at the lower right, in cursive writing: *ingres fils*.

CONDITION:       The drawing is in an extraordinarily fine state of preservation.

PROVENANCE:      In 1886, the Goupil Collection; said to have been in London with the heirs of the Goupil family; les Quatre Chemins, Paris, to John S. Newberry, 1958.

BIBLIOGRAPHY:    Edouard Forestié, *Jean-Marie-Joseph Ingres Père, Peintre et Sculpteur*, Montauban, 1886, p. 22 ff., reprod.

EXHIBITIONS:     Cambridge, Fogg Art Museum, 1960, *Thirty-three French Drawings from the Collection of John S. Newberry*, no. 17.

Little if anything definitive has been published up until now about the widely scattered, small rondel portraits which are inscribed "ingres fils." The three in the present exhibition, the preceding one, this, and No. 3, have been almost totally unknown. In addition, there is one in the Bonnat Collection, Bayonne (reprod. Lapauze, 1903, no. 90), traditionally called "Un Conventionnel." There were two formerly in the David Weill Collection (Gabriel Henriot, *Collection David Weill*, III, reprod. pp. 259 and 263). One of the David Weill drawings which is now in the Louvre bears the date "Le trois Juillet 1797" on the reverse. The other, which is in a private collection in London, is not dated.

The Fogg drawing has been known only in the poor reproduction which illustrated Edouard Forestié's regional monograph of 1886 (see above) devoted to the work of Ingres père, the tiny signature apparently not having been seen. There is, however, a finesse of expression and a surety and liveliness of touch hardly to be found in the stiff miniatures attributed to his father. There seems no reason to doubt the genuineness of the signature, "ingres fils." The sitter has not been identified. We presume that the drawing was made before Ingres left Toulouse for Paris.

*Fogg Art Museum, Harvard University,*
*Gift of John S. Newberry, in memory*
*of Meta P. Sachs, 1960.8*

Graphite on fine parchment (flesh side treated with lime wash), with black ink and green watercolor in the decorative border.

Diameter of the image: 3½ in. (99 mm.).* Diameter of the parchment: 5⁷⁄₁₆ in. (138 mm.).

Signed in black ink by the artist around the lower edge: *Ingres fils f. 13.7 bre 1796*

C<small>ONDITION</small>:     The drawing is very well preserved.

P<small>ROVENANCE</small>:     Jean Ningres, Toulouse; Henri Petiet, Paris, to Lessing Rosenwald, 1953.

B<small>IBLIOGRAPHY</small>:     Toulouse, Musée des Augustins, and Montauban, Musée Ingres, 1955, *Ingres et ses maîtres de Roques à David,* no. 169, where a photograph of the drawing was exhibited.

E<small>XHIBITIONS</small>:     Toulouse, Palais des Arts, 1939, *Cent cinquantième Anniversaire de la Révolution Française,* no. 121 (catalogue, special number of the *Bulletin Municipal*).

There seems no reason to doubt the inscription with its date. The drawing was made, therefore, in Toulouse a year before Ingres left for Paris. Obviously the youthful Ingres had been studying the rondel profile portraits of Charles-Nicolas Cochin and had been influenced by them, even to the extent of imitating Cochin's manner of signing and dating them.

In 1955, a reproduction of the drawing was exhibited with the well-known profile miniature portrait of Ingres' father from the Musée Ingres. It was then suggested that the Washington drawing (whose location at that time was unknown to the French) also represented Ingres père, a suggestion we find difficult to accept. Like the portrait from the Crocker Collection (see No. 1), it may depict another member of the Brochard troupe. The earring, an unconventional ornament for a gentleman in the late eighteenth century, suggests that this sitter may also be an actor.

*Lent by the National Gallery of Art, Washington, D. C., Rosenwald Collection*

Charcoal with extensive stumping on white wove paper. 15½ x 12⅝ in. (394 x 319 mm.)
Watermark: 353 within a circle.

Inscribed, in brown ink, at the lower left: *Ingres à Calamatta.* Illegible inscription in charcoal at the lower right: *44 x 84* (?).

Blind stamp of the Luigi Calamatta Collection at the lower center (L. 1717).

CONDITION:   When the drawing was removed from a former mount, a band approximately ⅞ in. wide along all four edges was seriously thinned from the back and, at intervals, torn. These very small areas have been extensively mended. The paper is lightly foxed.

PROVENANCE:   Luigi Calamatta (Sale, Paris, 18 December 1871, probably no. 135, p. 18); Edgar Degas (Sale, Paris, Galérie Georges Petit, 26-27 March 1918, no. 214, reprod. p. 95); Férault, Paris, to Grenville L. Winthrop, April, 1936.

BIBLIOGRAPHY:   Mongan, 1944, p. 403.

When the drawing came to the Fogg Art Museum with the Winthrop Bequest, it was called *Portrait of George Sand's Daughter* (?). For many years the question mark remained a mystery. Recently, however, the reason for the query was revealed in Mr. Winthrop's correspondence with Mr. Martin Birnbaum (Fogg Archives, letters from Mr. Birnbaum dated 20 February, 3 April and 17 April 1936). Mr. Birnbaum had seen the drawing in the spring of 1936 at Férault's in Paris and wrote enthusiastically to Mr. Winthrop, recommending its purchase. Férault, he said, was convinced that it represented George Sand's daughter. Undoubtedly, he meant George Sand's daughter-in-law, Lina Calamatta, who in 1862, married George Sand's son, Maurice Dudevant. A comparison, which we have made, between the drawing and Lina's portraits in the Carnavalet Museum, Paris, does indeed reveal a resemblance, one which we find fortuitous.

Mr. Birnbaum disagreed with Férault's identification of the sitter. He believed the drawing to be a very early one, in fact, one of the few surviving drawings made when Ingres was still a pupil in David's studio. Although we do not see the strong Raphaelesque character of which he spoke to Mr. Winthrop, we agree that the drawing is Davidian in style. It can be compared in scale and in time, as well as in the quality of line, to the portrait Ingres drew of his friend, Revoil (Bonnat Collection, Bayonne), when the latter was said to be eighteen years old. It is also very similar in touch and in the manner of drawing the eyes, to the so-called *Bonne des Desmoiselles Harvey,* Louvre. The latter is a fragment on the reverse of the double portrait of the Harvey sisters. Were that page not cut, it would be almost exactly the scale of the Winthrop drawing. Since the costume and kerchief in our drawing bear no clear relation to any known fashions of the time, we wonder if the young woman was a fellow pupil of Ingres in David's studio whom the student artist portrayed in her atelier dress.

Questions of chronology confirm this rejection of Férault's title. Marcelline-Claudine Calamatta, the engraver Calamatta's only daughter and Ingres' godchild, was born in the 1840's. Since the young lady in the drawing is at least twenty, were Lina the sitter, the drawing would have been executed in the sixties, an impossibility in terms of style. The inscription *Ingres à Calamatta,* written in pen in a cursive script, is in Ingres' own hand, but it is not his early signature. Presumably Ingres signed the drawing many years after it was made, undoubtedly at the time he presented it to his friend who had seen it and admired it in the studio.

*Fogg Art Museum, Harvard University,*
*Bequest of Grenville L. Winthrop, 1943.844*

Ingres à Calamatta

Graphite on tracing paper which has been affixed to two layers of wove paper; white chalk heightening in the eyes of Mlle. Forestier (perhaps by a later hand?). 11⅛ x 14⅝ in. (300 x 372 mm.)

Signed at the lower left: *Ingres f. 1804*

Inscribed in Ingres' hand at lower center: *famille de Mr forestier ancien juge de S. Nicolas à Paris*

CONDITION:     The tracing paper has darkened severely. At some time prior to the final mounting the four corners were damaged by glue; and three small losses to the left of the central axis, the largest ½ in. in width, have been repaired. Other minor punctures and abrasions, such as those retouched on the front foot of the spinet, are scattered across the sheet.

PROVENANCE:     Jean-Marie-Joseph Ingres (according to Lapauze); J. A. D. Ingres; presumably to Mme. Ingres, née Delphine Ramel (d. 1887); Sale of M . . . , Paris, Hôtel Drouot, 18 February 1884, no. 29; Fernand Guille, nephew of Mme. Ingres (according to Lapauze); Edgar Degas (Sale, Paris, Georges Petit Gallery, 26-27 March 1918, no. 208, reprod. p. 91); Scott & Fowles, New York, to Grenville L. Winthrop, January, 1922.

BIBLIOGRAPHY:     Albert Magimel, *Oeuvres de J. A. Ingres,* Paris, 1851, pl. 5, after the engraving by Reveil; Delaborde, 1870, p. 297 (probably cited under no. 301); Blanc, 1870, p. 8 (?); Lapauze, 1901, p. 265; Lapauze, 1903, p. 48, cited under no. 20; Lapauze, 1910, p. 112, fn. 1; Lapauze, 1911, p. 60; Charles Martine, *Ingres, Dessins de maîtres français,* Paris, 1926, cited under no. 14; Mongan, 1944, pp. 388-90; Mongan, 1947, no. 1, reprod.; Alazard, 1950, p. 144, fn. 19; *Dessins d'Ingres du Musée de Montauban,* Musée Ingres, Montauban, 1951, (p. 15), cited under no. 9; Toulouse, Musée des Augustins, and Montauban, Musée Ingres, 1955, *Ingres et ses maîtres,* cited under no. 103; Ternois, 1959, cited above, no. 54.

In the center stands Julie Forestier, the gifted young lady to whom Ingres was engaged when he left for Rome. According to her birth certificate, Julie, an only child, was born on 13 June 1782, five years after her parents' marriage. At the Salon of 1804, the year of this drawing, she exhibited a painting entitled *Minerva, Goddess of Wisdom and Fine Arts.* Her engagement to Ingres was broken in 1808; her father considered Ingres' interest in his daughter inadequate. Later Julie wrote her version of the events in a thinly veiled roman à clef, *Emma ou la Fiancée,* first published by Lapauze in 1910.

Three versions of this group-portrait survive. In addition to this one, there is one in the Louvre, signed and dated 1806, and another at Montauban with neither date nor signature. According to Lapauze, Ingres made the Louvre drawing as a parting gift for Julie when he left for Rome, a second one for himself to take to Rome, and a third, a tracing, for his father who in June, 1806, had promoted his son's suit.

The version which Ingres had given Julie in 1806, she gave back when the engagement was broken. Ingres later presented this version to his friend Louis-Joseph-Auguste Coutan (d. 1830). Coutan's heirs presented it to the Louvre in 1883. The second version belonged to Lapauze (he claimed not to know its provenance) who bequeathed it, in 1928, to the Ingres Museum at Montauban. The Fogg tracing, which had belonged to Ingres' father and which presumably returned to the artist after his father's death, Ingres is said to have given to his nephew, Fernand-Marie-François Guille (d. 1908). It was in the Degas Sale in 1918.

Lapauze seems not to have known or observed that the Fogg version is dated 1804, with an inscription in Ingres' own writing identifying the sitters. It has been equally unknown that the drawing passed through a sale at the Hôtel Drouot, 18 February 1884, with Haro, père and fils, as experts. The inscription was then noted. Haro père writes in the catalogue, "J'ai vu ce dessin chez Monsieur Ingres, mon maître, pendant plus de trente ans; il en existe un autre dans la collection

légué au Louvre par la famille Hauguet" (a year before he writes). The catalogue of the sale does not specify whether the drawing is a tracing or not. We do not know who purchased it at the 1884 sale. It may have been then that Degas acquired it.

Although on tracing paper, the Fogg version is not an exact tracing of either the Louvre or the Montauban version. The three versions vary somewhat in size (Louvre: 9¼ x 12⅝ in.; Montauban: 9½ x 12¾ in.; Fogg: 9½ x 13⅞ in.). The figures in the Louvre drawing are the same breadth but not the same height as those in the Fogg tracing. It would not have been difficult for Ingres to have broadened his composition by moving the tracing to the right as he drew, thus widening the space between Julie and the piano. It is difficult, however, to explain the differences in the height of the figures. In the Fogg version they are somewhat taller than in the other two. (For example, Julie is 7¾ in. high in the Montauban drawing, 8 in. in the Fogg's.)

Since Ingres knew the Forestier family as early as 1804, the date on the Fogg drawing could be as correct as the identification. In 1851, the painter Magimel, a friend of Ingres, brought out a volume devoted to Ingres' oeuvre. Curiously, it is the Fogg version which he reproduced in a line engraving by Reveil, but in the text he calls it the Coutan-Hauguet one. There are several proofs that Ingres made changes in his own works for the Magimel publication. Could he possibly have drawn the Fogg one expressly for Magimel? If he did so, why did he make such an elaborate drawing for such a poor line engraving? Could he, in 1851, have recreated his early manner of drawing? Not a single drawing which Ingres adapted for the Magimel publication is known, so it is impossible to make stylistic comparisons, and the question of date, therefore, must remain open. Because of the handling, however, we favor the early date.

*Fogg Art Museum, Harvard University,*
*Bequest of Grenville L. Winthrop, 1943.842*

Graphite on cream-colored wove paper. 9¼ x 7 in. (236 x 177 mm.)*

Signed at the lower right: *Ingres fecit | in Roma. | 1806*

CONDITION:     Although the drawing was treated in 1946, it remains somewhat discolored. A pale oval stain still indicates the window of a former mount.

PROVENANCE:     Thomas-Charles Naudet (d. 1810); Naudet family; Anonymous sale, Paris, Hôtel Drouot, 9 March 1918, no. 181; Henry Lapauze (Sale, Paris, Hôtel Drouot, 21 June 1929, no. 20, reprod.); Rhode Island School of Design, 1929.

REPRODUCTIONS: Engraved in 1808 by Caroline Naudet, the artist's sister.

BIBLIOGRAPHY:     References to the engravings are included in this listing. Delaborde, 1870, no. 383; Blanc, 1870, p. 246; Henri Beraldi, *Les graveurs du XIXᵉ siècle,* Paris, 1890, x, pp. 191, 193; Lapauze, 1901, p. 267; Lapauze, 1910, p. 87 ff.; Lapauze, 1911, p. 78, engraving reprod. p. 77; Lapauze, *Briant,* 1911, p. 48; Charles Saunier, "Exposition Ingres," *Les Arts,* July, 1911, engraving reprod. p. 4; Thieme-Becker, xxv, 1931, "Naudet"; Miller, 1938, p. 14, fn. 25; Naef, 1960, pp. 15, 118; Naef, 1967, fn. 5.

Thomas-Charles Naudet was born in Paris in 1773. A pupil of Hubert Robert, he was trained in the late eighteenth-century tradition of landscape painting and drawing. He was in Rome in 1806, after having made many panoramic landscape drawings in the north of Italy for a contemplated *Voyage pittoresque et historique du Nord de l'Italie.* Ingres arrived in Rome in October, 1806. By the beginning of 1807 the two artists were already good friends. It was to Naudet that Ingres entrusted the drawings and the two painted rondels, now in Montauban, which were to show Julie the details of the setting in which he was living (see No. 7). In his letter of 12 January 1807 to Monsieur Forestier, Ingres begins: "La personne qui vous remet cette lettre est Monsieur Naudet, artiste paysagiste, très recommandé. . . . Monsieur Naudet a été, avec Granger, ma seule société depuis mon arrivée. Monsieur Naudet est un journal vivant du pays que j'habite. Je l'ai prié de vous en parler beaucoup, ce qu'il m'a promis." (Lapauze, 1910, pp. 88-89.)

Naudet left Rome in January, 1807, reaching Paris in February and delivering the drawings and landscape paintings sent by Ingres. Unfortunately, the promise of his youth was not fulfilled. He died in Paris of tuberculosis in July, 1810. The book for which his landscape illustrations were drawn was published in Paris ten years later by Didot.

In this delightful drawing he sits on a grassy hummock, a sketch pad on his knee, his pencil ready to draw, a bemused expression on his charming and witty if not handsome face.

*Museum of Art, Rhode Island School of Design*

Verso: Sketches of a basin and the capital and base of a column.

Graphite on thin white wove paper. 4¾ x 7⅞ in. (120 x 200 mm.)

Watermark: R WII. | 18 ... (R. Williams?)

Inscribed to the left of center: *vue de la villa medicis | de ma croisée de Saint Gaetano. | et de la trinité du mont.* Inscribed at the lower right: *à Rome. 1807.* The notations on the verso are not legible.

The old mount bore two collectors' marks: Paul Mathey (L. 2100$^b$) and Louis Godefroy (L. 2971$^a$).

CONDITION:      The drawing has been removed from its former backing.

PROVENANCE:    Paul Mathey; Louis Godefroy; Charles P. Curtis; Maynard Walker; J. K. Tannhauser Gallery; Richard Davis; John S. Newberry.

BIBLIOGRAPHY:  Louis Godefroy, *Estampes et dessins,* Paris, 1924, p. 54, no. 233, reprod.; Louis Godefroy, *Estampes et dessins,* Paris, 1926, p. 73, no. 696; Alazard, 1950, pp. 35 and 144, fn. 4, Ch. III; pl. x; Naef, 1958, p. 14, no. 4; Naef, 1960, p. 123, no. 31, fig. 9; *Emporium,* CXXXIV, July, 1961, p. 29, reprod. p. 30.

EXHIBITIONS:   Springfield, etc., 1939-40, no. 31; New York, Willard Gallery, 1956, *A Group of Exceptional Drawings,* no. 12, reprod.; Cambridge, Fogg Art Museum, 1960, *Thirty-three French Drawings from the Collection of John S. Newberry,* no. 18.

When Ingres reached Rome in October, 1806, he was obviously deeply moved, as others both before and after him have been, by the light, grandeur and design of Rome. He was still in love with Julie Forestier, the fiancée he had left in Paris (see No. 5). To make Julie aware of the setting in which he found himself, Ingres painted two small rondel landscapes, now at Montauban, and made a series of landscape drawings showing the Villa Medici, its gardens, and the Pavilion of S. Gaetano, a square four-story tower at the west end of the Villa's gardens where he had his room and studio. His friend, Thomas-Charles Naudet (see No. 6), a landscape painter, who was leaving for Paris in January, 1807, was charged with the delivery of the package to Julie. Other drawings followed a little later, but correspondence ceased between Ingres and the Forestier family in August, 1808. If, as seems probable, this was a drawing sent to Paris to show his setting, then it must date before 1808. It probably was made in early January, 1807.

   Two drawings in Montauban made from the garden showing the Pavilion of S. Gaetano have a pale brown wash added. This view, out of a window facing east, is towards the Villa. A drawing at Montauban from a slightly different perspective (one floor below?) but from the same angle repeats this as the left half of the composition, but carries the panorama to the right as far as the Torre delle Milizie (Naef, 1960, no. 32).

*Fogg Art Museum, Harvard University,*
*Gift of John S. Newberry in memory*
*of Meta P. Sachs, 1961.9*

vue de la villa medici
de ma croisée de Sant Gaetano.
et de la trinité du mont.

à Rome . 1807.

Graphite on white laid paper. 5¼ x 3⅛ in. (133 x 79 mm.)*

Ingres made notes on the drawing. Although they have been erased, enough remains so that one can recognize his unmistakable handwriting; one can even decipher part of what was written at the right, near the nose: *bien plus p* ... and in the sitter's ruffle: *plus.* ... Inscribed on the mount by Achille Leclère: *ingres. f. Rome 1808 | portrait de Bury architecte.* (The 8 is superimposed over a 7.)

PROVENANCE:    Achille Leclère; Leclère heirs; Claude Darton, Avignon; Lucien Goldschmidt, New York, to Mrs. Jacob M. Kaplan, 1964.

BIBLIOGRAPHY:    Lucien Goldschmidt, *Architecture and the Achille Leclère-Ingres Sketchbook* (Catalogue no. 32), New York, 1964, no. 124, reprod.; Daniel Ternois, "L'Ingrisme dans le monde," *Bulletin de Musée Ingres,* Montauban, September, 1964, p. 21; Hans Naef, "L'Ingrisme dans le monde," *Bulletin du Musée Ingres,* Montauban, July, 1965, p. 21; Naef, 1967, no. 3, pl. 2.

Antoine-François-Desiré Girard de Bury was born in Paris in 1780 and died there 5 December 1862. He entered the École des Beaux-Arts in 1794 and won a second Grand Prize for architecture in 1802. Through the interest of the school's director, who admired his excellent character, he was given a special recommendation which permitted him to be accepted, although only a second prize winner, as a student at the Villa Medici, much to the joy of his contemporaries who seem to have shared their superior's estimation of his character and worth. Bury became a close friend of Ingres at the Academy in Rome, and even assisted him in making a background drawing for the earliest version of the *Stratonice.* In a letter from Rome to M. Forestier (21 February 1807), Ingres describes Bury as a pupil of Charles Percier. Curiously, although he lived a long time, little if anything seems to be known about his later career.

In his most recent article (*op. cit.*) in which he discusses this drawing, Dr. Naef suggests that possibly its extraordinary size and shape is to be explained either by its presence in the album, for which it was perhaps originally drawn, or that, in the light of the changed last digit, it may have been copied in 1808 from a (now unknown) portrait of 1807. We would like to suggest a third possibility: i.e., that it is the cut down left half of a double portrait of a pair of architects similar to the Smith College *Leclère and Provost* (No. 23).

*Mrs. Jacob M. Kaplan, New York City*

Graphite on white wove paper. 10⅜ x 6⅞ in. (270 x 215 mm.)

Signed at the lower right: *Ingres.*

CONDITION:     The drawing which was badly discolored when it entered the collection was bleached in
               1949.

PROVENANCE:    Arsène Alexandre (Sale, Georges Petit Gallery, Paris, 18-19 May 1903, no. 138, reprod.);
               Count Allard du Chollet; Alfred Beurdeley (Sale, Paris, 2-4 June 1920, no. 225, p. 70, re-
               prod. opp. p. 70) to Gobin; Grenville L. Winthrop.

BIBLIOGRAPHY:  *Apollon,* St. Petersburg, 1912, IV, pl. 7, pp. 16-17; *Société de reproductions des dessins de
               maîtres,* 1912, pl. 13; Mongan, 1944, p. 392, pl. 390; Agnes Mongan, "Find the Artist," *Art
               News,* L, March, 1951, p. 20; p. 66, reprod. pl. 2.

EXHIBITIONS:   Paris, Grand Palais, 1905, *Salon d'automne,* p. 189, no. 61; St. Petersburg, 1912, *Exposi-
               tion centennale de l'art français,* no. 662.

Marie-Joseph-Honorée Vanzenne was born ca. 1763. She was the second wife of Guillon Lethière, the painter (see Nos. 19 and 30), in a marriage which was her second union. Guillon Lethière took over as Director of the French Academy in October, 1807, a year after Ingres' arrival. From the first, the Guillon Lethières were kind to the young Montalbanais. He may even have known them in Paris (see letter of 7 April 1807, to Monsieur Forestier, *Roman d'Amour*).

Little is mentioned concerning Mme. Lethière in the known records of the time, but obviously Ingres found her a sympathetic personality. He has recorded her short plump figure with insight and extraordinary discretion. He was, it is clear, tolerantly amused by her love of finery.

The sitter was identified by Dr. Naef.

*Fogg Art Museum, Harvard University,*
*Bequest of Grenville L. Winthrop, 1943 858*

Ingres.

PORTRAIT OF MADAME GUILLAUME GUILLON LETHIÈRE AND HER SON LUCIEN

Graphite on cream-colored wove rag paper. 9½ x 7$\frac{5}{16}$ in. (243 x 188 mm.)*

Signed and dated in the lower right corner: *Ingres rome | 1808*

Inscribed on the reverse of the drawing: *pour ma fille | serviere.*

Stamp of the Metropolitan Museum at the lower left.

CONDITION: The drawing has suffered minor losses along its edges. A tear approximately 1½ in. long, leading down from the upper edge to the left of center, has been mended. The paper, once discolored, has been bleached to approximately its original color.

PROVENANCE: Paris, Private Collection; H. O. Havemeyer.

BIBLIOGRAPHY: R. H. Wilenski, *French Painting,* Boston, 1931, p. 198, pl. 82; H. O. Havemeyer Collection, *Catalogue of Paintings, Prints, Sculptures and Objects of Art,* 1931, p. 190, reprod. p. 10; John Rewald, "Ingres and the Camera," *Art News,* XLII, May, 1943, reprod. p. 10; Bryan Holme, *Master Drawings,* New York/London, 1944, p. 13, pl. 93; Mongan, 1944, p. 392; Mongan, 1947, no. 2, reprod.; Shoolman and Slatkin, 1950, p. 110, pl. 62; Alazard, 1950, pl. 27; Naef, 1960, p. 27, no. 52.

EXHIBITIONS: New York, Metropolitan Museum, 1930, *The H. O. Havemeyer Collection,* no. 190, reprod.; Springfield, etc. 1939-40, no. 38; San Francisco, California Palace of the Legion of Honor, 1947, *19th Century French Drawings,* no. 1, reprod.; Philadelphia, Philadelphia Museum of Art, 1950-51, *Masterpieces of Drawing,* no. 82, reprod.; Rotterdam, Paris, New York, 1958-59, no. 127, pl. 101.

The sitters have been identified recently by Dr. Naef. Madame Guillaume Guillon Lethière (see No. 9) is shown with her son Lucien, born in Paris in 1802. They are represented standing in the garden of the Villa Medici, with the Villa behind them at the left and the Santissima Trinità dei Monti at the right. This double portrait and the portrait of Lucien Bonaparte (No. 11) are the earliest with Roman landscape backgrounds.

Lucien died in Haiti in 1832.

*The Metropolitan Museum of Art,*
*Bequest of Mrs. H. O. Havemeyer, 1929,*
*The H. O. Havemeyer Collection*

Graphite on white wove paper. 9⅜ x 7⅛ in. (236 x 185 mm.)

Signed at the lower right, possibly by another hand, in graphite softer than that used for the drawing:
*Ingres*

PROVENANCE:    Lucien Bonaparte (d. 1840); Charles de Chatillon (d. 1843); Anonymous private collector to H. R. Stirlin, Saint-Prex, Switzerland, 1928; Wildenstein, New York, to John Goelet, 1963.

BIBLIOGRAPHY:    Jean-Gabriel Goulinat, "Ingres et la couleur," *L'Art et les artistes,* xv, January, 1928, reprod. p. 113; Jean-Paul Alaux, *L'Académie de France à Rome,* Paris, ii, 1933, reprod. p. 163 (as "Le peintre Isabey"); Jean Cassou, "Ingres," *L'Art et les artistes,* February, 1936, reprod. p. 147 (as "Portrait d'homme"); Hans Naef, "Vier Ingres-Zeichnungen," *Pantheon,* viii, 1960, pp. 36-40, reprod. p. 39; Cornelius Vermeule, *European Art and the Classical Past,* Cambridge, 1964, p. 192, fn. 21; Naef, 1967, fn. 5, to be published.

EXHIBITIONS:    Zurich, Kunsthaus Zurich, 1937, *Zeichnungen französischer Meister von David zu Millet,* not in catalogue; Geneva, Musée Rath, 1954, *Trésors des collections romandes,* no. 238 (as "Portrait de Marquis de Chatillon"); Zurich, Kunsthaus Zurich, 1958, *Rome vue par Ingres,* no. B.3.

Lucien, Napoleon's most gifted brother, was six years his junior. The relations between the two were often strained. Lucien preferred to live in Rome where Ingres met him in 1807, probably through Guillon Lethière who was Lucien's agent. The younger Bonaparte was a passionate collector of paintings and antiquities and is appropriately represented by Ingres in the Forum. Dr. Vermeule points out (*op. cit.*) that Lucien is seated on a Roman cinerarium with the Quirinal in the background. He is seen from the Villa Malta, with the Torre delle Milizie in the left background. Although not dated, the drawing must have been made, according to the costume, about 1807-08.

The drawing was formerly thought to be a portrait of Charles de Chatillon, an artist of modest talent attached to Lucien's household. The confusion probably arose because at one time the drawing seems to have belonged to him. Dr. Naef (*op. cit.*) has re-established the sitter's identity.

*John Goelet, New York City*

Graphite on white wove paper. 7¾ x 14⁵⁄₁₆ in. (197 x 364 mm.)

Watermark on the support: H. Dobbs 1805

Signed at the lower left: *Ing*

Stamp of Metropolitan Museum of Art at the lower right.

CONDITION:     The paper has been rounded at the corners and inlaid into a piece of white laid paper. A large hole near the lower left (including the cheek and chin of the lower head) has been patched. The drawing has also suffered as a result of foxing and liquid stains.

PROVENANCE:     Edouard Gatteaux (d. 1881); Edouard Dubufe; François Flameng (Sale, Paris, Georges Petit Gallery, 26-27 May 1919, no. 126) to the Metropolitan Museum of Art, New York.

BIBLIOGRAPHY:     Gatteaux, pl. 45; Bryson Burroughs, "Recent Accessions: Drawings by Ingres," *Metropolitan Museum of Art Bulletin,* November, 1919, pp. 246-47; *European Drawings II,* New York, Metropolitan Museum, n.d., no. 38, reprod.; Jacob Bean, *100 European Drawings in the Metropolitan Museum of Art,* New York, 1965, no. 64, reprod.

EXHIBITIONS:     Paris, 1867, no. 177; Paris, 1911, no. 191.

*Romulus Conqueror of Acron* was one of the two paintings ordered by General Miollis to decorate the Quirinal. Like the other, *Ossian* (No. 17), it was a subject upon which Ingres had begun work even before he received the commission in 1810.

This superb page of studies from the Metropolitan is clearly related to the large Louvre drawing, signed and dated 1808 (Gatteaux, pl. 58). In fact, it must have preceded it; for the Acron in that composition lies with his arms over his head, as in the lower of the two heads here, his eyes closed, his legs slightly drawn up, as they are in the lowest of the figures. A page in the Musée Bonnat, Bayonne, with studies of the two young men who precede Romulus, the shield bearer and the boy with the helmet, also seems to be connected with this early composition (Gatteaux, pl. 25), as do two separate studies of the same figures (Gatteaux, pl. 44, present whereabouts unknown). A page with two powerful nude studies for the soldier bending over Acron is also at Bayonne.

Another group of drawings makes it possible to follow the subsequent development of the theme. A large pen and ink drawing, signed and dated 1810 (Louvre; Giraudon, 13269), brings the composition nearer the completed work. The seascape has been eliminated, the horses face the other way, Romulus is bearded and Acron has only his right arm over his head. His left lies across his body, as it does in the painting. A drawing which shows Ingres trying out this pose (there are four arms sketched) is also at Bayonne (Giraudon, 13444), as is a page with a detail of the head and arm of Romulus and his left leg and foot and his right foot. The fact that the head is inscribed, in Ingres' hand, "la tête de monte cavallo" would seem to connect this drawing with the later studies. A full-length nude study for the youth with the Romulus and Remus shield (Gatteaux, pl. 18) and one with studies of the trumpeter (Gatteaux, pl. 52) are also for the painting.

One more celebrated drawing is connected with the painting, a work that shows Ingres revealing an unexpected sense of humor. The artist represented himself working on the picture, a tiny figure seated before the huge canvas under the frescoed arches of the tribune of Sta. Trinità dei Monti which was temporarily his studio. His famous violin rests against a chair behind him (Musée Bonnat, Bayonne, reprod. Lapauze, 1911, p. 125). A pencil drawing of the whole composition was recently on the New York art market.

The disastrous campaign of 1812 in Russia changed many plans. Napoleon never went to Rome. Placed in the Lateran Palace in 1815, the painting was presented to Napoleon III in 1867 by Pius IX. It hangs today in the École des Beaux-Arts, Paris.

*Metropolitan Museum of Art,*
*Rogers Fund, 1919*

Graphite on white wove paper.  11¼ x 8¾ in.  (284 x 222 mm.)

Watermark: J WHATMAN.

CONDITION:     The drawing has suffered from recurrent foxing and other stains, and has therefore been
               bleached. There is a minor tear along the upper right edge of the sheet.

PROVENANCE:    Jean-Louis Robin to M. Mérandon, Autun; Amaury-Duval to his student Eugène Fro-
               ment-Delormel; Mme. Mazeran, née Froment, to her cousin Maurice Bouts; Anonymous
               Sale, Hôtel Drouot, Paris, 29 June 1927, no. 31, to C. de Hauke; Mrs. Emily Crane Chad-
               bourne, Washington.

BIBLIOGRAPHY:  Delaborde, 1870, no. 409, p. 312; Lapauze, *Briant,* 1911, p. 48, reprod. p. 51; Zabel, 1930,
               no. 6, reprod. p. 379; Alazard, 1950, p. 36; Naef, 1960, p. 27, fn. 52; Frederick Cummings,
               "Romantic Portraitist, Three Drawings by Ingres," *Bulletin of the Detroit Institute of
               Arts,* XLIV, 1965, pl. 70.

EXHIBITIONS:   Chicago, Art Institute of Chicago, 1961, *Drawings from the Collection of the Art Insti-
               tute of Chicago,* no. 86; New York, Wildenstein, 1963, *Master Drawings from the Art
               Institute of Chicago,* no. 76, pl. 31.

Jean-Louis Robin, who was born in Nevers in 1775 and died in that city in 1846, was a doctor attached most of his life to the French army as a surgeon. Between 1806 and 1815 he was with Napoleon's army on twelve campaigns. In 1806 he was in Italy; in 1808 he was in Rome under General
Miollis (see No. 21); in 1809 he was in Austria with the Emperor, but returned to Italy in 1811 and
1812 under Eugène Beauharnais. In 1812-13 he was in Russia with Napoleon. These biographical
details suggest a possible date for the portrait, for it seems probable that it was General Miollis who
introduced him to the artist and that this brilliant portrait was made at the time Ingres was first in
contact with the General, that is ca. 1808-09.

Ingres drew Dr. Robin on the parapet of the Villa Medici, with a view of St. Peter's behind him.

*The Art Institute of Chicago,
Gift of Mrs. Emily Crane Chadbourne*

Hard graphite on white wove paper. $10\frac{9}{16}$ x $8\frac{5}{16}$ in. (268 x 212 mm.)

Signed at the lower right: *Ingres fecit | roma 1809*

CONDITION:     The paper has yellowed slightly as a result of age and exposure to light. A diffuse brown
               stain appears at the upper right.

PROVENANCE:    Presumably M. Mallet (d. 1853); a "member of Royal House of Wurttemberg"(?); Bar-
               oness Wilhelm-Carl von Rothschild, née Matilde von Rothschild (d. 1924); Goldschmidt-
               Rothschild family; Dr. Jacob Hirsch, New York, to the Art Institute of Chicago, Charles
               Deering Collection, 1938.

REPRODUCTIONS: Engraving by Angelo Boucheron, completed by Claude-Marie-François Dien.

BIBLIOGRAPHY:  Delaborde, 1870, no. 359; Blanc, 1870, p. 246; Lapauze, 1901, p. 267; Lapauze, 1911, p. 98,
               engraving reprod.; Lapauze, *Briant,* 1911, p. 48; Miller, 1938, p. 14, fn. 25, p. 15; D. C.
               Rich, "Monsieur Mallet by Ingres," *Bulletin of the Art Institute of Chicago,* XXXII, Septem-
               ber-October, 1939, p. 66 ff., reprod.; Alazard, 1950, p. 37, pl. XVIII; Kurt Seligmann, "A
               Letter about Drawing," *The Art Institute of Chicago Quarterly,* XLVI, 15 September 1952,
               p. 45, reprod.; Ternois, 1959, p. 83; Naef, 1960, p. 27, fn. 52.

EXHIBITIONS:   Springfield, etc., 1939-40, not listed in the catalogue; Chicago, Art Institute of Chicago,
               1946, *Drawings Old and New,* no. 30, reprod.; Paris, Musée de l'Orangerie, 1955, *De
               David à Toulouse-Lautrec,* no. 80, pl. 5; Chicago, Art Institute of Chicago, 1961, *Fiftieth
               Anniversary Exhibition,* no. 85; New York, Wildenstein, 1963, *Drawings from the Art
               Institute of Chicago,* no. 75.

Charles-François Mallet was born in Paris in 1766 and died there in 1853. He completed his training
as a civil engineer in 1791, and in 1805 was placed in charge of road and bridge construction under
King Joseph Bonaparte in Naples. Shortly afterwards he held a similar post in the departments of
the Doria and the Po in North Italy. It is therefore very appropriate that Ingres has chosen to represent M. Mallet standing on the banks of the Tiber near the Ponte Rotto, with the Ponte Fabrizio in
the background. Above the right arch of the bridge we see the cupola of S. Carlo ai Catinari and,
nearer to us, the campanile of S. Nicolà in Carceri.

There is no family relationship between the M. Mallet of this drawing and the Madame Mallet
of another drawing by Ingres in a French private collection. Because the latter is dated 1809, it has
often been mistakenly said to be the pendant of the drawing of Charles-François Mallet.

*The Art Institute of Chicago,*
*The Charles Deering Collection*

Ingres. fecit
roma 1809.

Hard graphite on thin white wove paper. 6⅞ x 5½ in. (180 x 140 mm.)*

Signed at the lower left: *Ingres* | *a rome 1809*

CONDITION:    The paper has darkened slightly.

PROVENANCE:    Merry-Joseph Blondel (d. 1853) to his widow, Mme. Blondel, née Louise-Émilie Delafontaine; to their daughter Mme. Alfred Wittersheim, née Émilie-Louise-Eudoxie Blondel; Wittersheim family; Wildenstein, New York, to Mrs. Grace Rainey Rogers, 1940.

BIBLIOGRAPHY:    Galichon, 1861, p. 46; Delaborde, 1870, no. 261; Blanc, 1870, p. 235; Gonin, 1888, p. 14; Louise Burroughs, "Drawings by Ingres," *Metropolitan Museum Bulletin*, IV, February, 1946, p. 161, reprod.; Mongan, 1947, no. 3, reprod.; Naef, 1960, p. 27, fn. 52.

EXHIBITIONS:    Paris, 1861; Paris, 1867, no. 548; San Francisco, 1947, no. 4, reprod. p. 14; New York, 1961, not in catalogue.

Merry-Joseph Blondel was born in Paris in 1781. His father was a simple house-painter, yet the family had several connections with the arts. A brother was an architect; a sister married a well-known decorator and architect; and after the death of his first wife, Merry-Joseph himself married, in 1832, the daughter of a noted maker of bronzes who was also a painter, Pierre-Maximilien Delafontaine. It was Delafontaine who willed to the Musée des Arts Decoratifs the small rondel oil landscape by Ingres, the so-called *Casino of Raphael*.

Although the uncle for whom Merry-Joseph was named wished him to become a notary, after two years in a notary's office, the young Blondel beseeched his father to rescue him. His father then apprenticed him to a painter of porcelains where Blondel learned figure drawing and ornament design. Having made remarkable progress, he left the porcelain painter's to enter Regnault's atelier. In 1802 he won five prizes. The next year, 1803, he won the *premier prix de Rome;* but he only left for Italy in 1809, the year of this drawing.

The portrait is an extraordinary likeness, as Blondel's *Self-Portrait* of 1817 clearly demonstrates (*Société de l'histoire de l'art français,* 1936, reprod. opp. p. 80). The similarity is further reinforced by Blondel's strongly "Ingresque" style. His friend had obviously exerted a decisive influence upon the development of Blondel's sense of color, design and handling of paint.

The friendship between Ingres and Blondel, formed when they were fellow students in Rome, was renewed in the same city in 1839. Blondel and his wife then spent four months at the Villa Medici as guests of Ingres and his wife. At the close of the visit the two couples made a journey together to Ancona, Loretto, Assisi and Urbino. They parted with reluctance, the Blondels continuing their journey back to Paris, while Ingres and his wife returned to Rome. Blondel, who had assumed Guillon Lethière's chair at the Académie des Beaux-Arts in 1832, wished to be Ingres' successor as Director of the Villa Medici. His candidacy, although supported by Ingres, was not successful; the position went to Schnetz.

The Fogg Museum possesses nineteen drawings by Blondel. Eleven came in the Leclère Album (see No. 8), eight in the album given by Claude Darton in 1963.

*The Metropolitan Museum of Art,*
*Bequest of Grace Rainey Rogers, 1943*

Graphite on white wove paper. Diameter: 6⅞ in. (174 mm.)

Signed and dated at the left: *Par Ingres | a Rome | 1809*

CONDITION:       The paper has darkened with age and exposure to light.

PROVENANCE:      Henri-Joseph Ruxthiel; Mme. Hortense Petry, his daughter by his first wife; Mme. Amé-
                 lie Duguey, his daughter by his second wife; Lucien Duguey (d. 1936); the sitter's de-
                 scendants to John Goelet, 1961.

REPRODUCTIONS:   Lithograph by Henri-Gérard Fontallard. As the lithograph gives the date of Ruxthiel's
                 death, 1837, it cannot be earlier than that year.

BIBLIOGRAPHY:    P. J. Goetghebuer, *Notice sur Henri-Joseph Ruxthiel,* Ghent, 1851 (special issue of the
                 *Annales de la Société des Beaux-Arts de Gand*), p. 7, reprod. as frontispiece; Delaborde,
                 1870, no. 410; Blanc, 1870, p. 239; Jouin, 1888, p. 171; Lapauze, 1901, p. 268; Thieme-
                 Becker, XXIX, 1935, "Ruxthiel"; Naef, 1967, no. 4, pl. 3.

EXHIBITION:      Paris, 1867, no. 388.


Henri-Joseph Ruxthiel (also spelled Rutschiel, Ruthiel) was born in Lierneux, Belgium, in 1775 and
died in Paris in 1837. He went to Rome in 1809 as a winner of the *prix de Rome* in sculpture. Belgium was then under French domination, so he could qualify as a French student. As Dr. Naef has
found (*op. cit.*), Ruxthiel had a curious history, for he was a simple shepherd carving crooks (according to local legend) until the moment two passing hunters made his acquaintance in the
woods, saw his talent and placed him in a school at Liège. Paris followed and then Rome. His early
promise was not fulfilled. He seems to have been notably successful financially and in his collecting, which was wide and varied; but the quality of his work left much to be desired. A contemporary
described him as "homely, grimacing, of unattractive appearance, but keen, adroit and clever"
(Naef, *op. cit.*)—just as Ingres saw him.

*John Goelet, New York City*

Par Ingres
à Rome
1809.

Watercolor (blue, pinkish violet and gray) with pen and brown ink over graphite, heightened with white gouache, on white wove paper which has been affixed to white board. 9¾ x 7¾ in. (247 x 187 mm.)

Signed in blue watercolor at the lower right: *Ingres in E Pinx Roma 1809*

CONDITION:    The drawing is very well preserved.

PROVENANCE:    de Beaumont; Grenville L. Winthrop, 1935.

BIBLIOGRAPHY:    J. F. Le Sueur, *Ossian ou les bardes,* Paris, 1804; Mongan, 1944, p. 404, fig. 14, p. 405; Agnes Mongan, "Ingres and the Antique," *Journal of the Warburg and Courtauld Institutes,* x, 1947, p. 12, pl. 86; Schlenoff, 1956, p. 79, fn. 2; Daniel Ternois, "Ingres et le Songe d'Ossian," *Walter Friedlaender zum 90. Geburtstag,* Berlin, 1965, pp. 185-92; Daniel Ternois, *Ingres et son temps, Montauban, Musée Ingres, Peintures* (Inventaire des collections publiques françaises, 11), Paris, 1965, p. 156, no. 157.

When *Ossian* first appeared in a French translation in 1801 (Didot), its success was immediate. Poets, composers and painters were inspired by the poem (published by James Macpherson in 1762-63) and its romantic themes of bravery in battle. At the Salon of 1802, Girodet exhibited *Ossian Receiving the French Heroes,* a painting Ingres, who admired Girodet greatly, could well have seen before he left Paris in 1806.

Not only are there several pages in Ingres' notebooks devoted to details of the theme (quoted by Schlenhoff, *op. cit.,* p. 76, fn. 2), but there is another source, a musical one, which would have appealed to him. *Ossian ou les bardes,* an opera in five acts with music by J. F. Le Sueur and libretto by Dercy and Deschamps, was first presented at the Imperial Academy of Music in 1804 (see Mongan, *op. cit.,* p. 12). Ingres, who was still in Paris in 1804, undoubtedly saw the production, for his composition follows the libretto (Act IV, scene iii). Ingres himself later said that it was Le Sueur who first taught him, when he was young, to appreciate great music.

It was well known that the poem was a favorite of Napoleon's. Le Sueur seems to have been aware of this, for in 1803 he dedicated his opera to the First Consul. In 1811, when Ingres was commissioned to paint a decoration for the bedroom of the Quirinal Palace which Napoleon was expected to occupy, the choice of Ossian seemed appropriate. The fact that the Fogg watercolor is signed and dated *1809* suggests that Ingres had been busy with the subject before the commission was given. Indeed, General Miollis, a childhood friend of Ingres' fellow artist Granger, may have known this when he transmitted the order.

Napoleon never reached Rome. In 1836, Ingres bought back the painting with the intention of reworking it, but got no further than turning it into a rectangle. It is now at Montauban.

The subject is a curiously Romantic and pre-Wagnerian one for the classic painter. The watercolor and painting are alike in their interpretation of the features and characters of the poem, but clearly not in the same style. We cannot agree with Ternois (*op. cit.*) that the Fogg watercolor was probably executed in the thirties or even later, and assigned an early date by the painter. In the details of the landscape and the handling of form it is characteristic of his earliest efforts in Rome.

Ossian, old, blind and grieving, dreams of the glorious past, summoning up in snowy moonlight the ghostly host of Celtic heroes. His dead son Oscar, wearing the helmet with the eagle's wing and carrying the shield called "The Voice of War," stands behind him. In Oscar's hand is the lance inherited from his grandfather, Fingal, to be used in the defense of the feeble and oppressed. At the left is Oscar's wife, the faithful Malvina. In the center background is Starno, the king of the Snows; ranged above him are the Celtic heroes, and below him, the bards (here female) playing on Irish harps. Unlike the other later versions (Louvre, Giraudon 13271, and Gatteaux, pl. 63) there is no mastiff in the Fogg watercolor.

*Fogg Art Museum, Harvard University,*
*Bequest of Grenville L. Winthrop, 1943.376*

Ingres in R. Rome 1808

Graphite on white wove paper. 10⅞ x 7⅛ in. (266 x 179 mm.)*

Signed at the lower right: *Ingres*

CONDITION:    The paper became brown as a result of exposure to light and contact with a secondary support to which it was formerly glued. That discoloration has been minimized by bleaching.

PROVENANCE:    Mme. Charles Hayard (d. 1854); Mme. Félix Duban, née Marguerite Hayard, the sitter's daughter (d. 1881); Mme. Frédéric Flachéron, née Caroline Hayard (d. 1894); her son, Félix Flachéron (d. 1927); Georges Bernheim, Paris; John Levy Galleries to Paul J. Sachs, January, 1922.

BIBLIOGRAPHY:    Delaborde, 1870, no. 323; Blanc, 1870, p. 237; Lapauze, 1911, reprod. p. 123; Exposition, 1921, reprod. p. 217; Ella S. Siple, "The Fogg Museum at Harvard," *Burlington Magazine*, L, June, 1927, p. 309, reprod. p. 307; Zabel, 1930, p. 381; Miller, 1938, p. 7, reprod.; Mongan-Sachs, 1940, no. 699, fig. 370; Mongan, 1947, no. 5, reprod.; Jean Cassou, *Ingres*, Brussels, 1947, pl. 34; René Huyghe and Philippe Jaccottet, *Le dessin français au XIXe siècle*, Lausanne, 1948, p. 173, reprod. p. 11; Alazard, 1950, p. 51, pl. XXII; Ternois, 1959, cited above no. 72; Tito Miotti, *Il collezionista di disegni*, Venice, 1962, fig. 101; H. Wade White, "Five Testimonials in the Bequest of Paul J. Sachs," *Fogg Art Museum Newsletter*, III, no. 1, October, 1965, p. 3, fig. 3; Hans Naef, "Ingres et la Famille Hayard," *Gazette des Beaux-Arts*, LXVII, January, 1966, pp. 37 ff., reprod. p. 39.

EXHIBITIONS:    Paris, 1867, no. 557; Paris, 1921, no. 71; Cambridge, 1929, no. 87; Springfield, etc., 1939-40, no. 44; San Francisco, 1947, no. 2; Detroit, Detroit Institute of Arts, 1951, *French Drawings of Five Centuries from the Collection of the Fogg Museum of Art*, no. 46, reprod.; Rotterdam, Paris, New York, 1958-59, no. 129, pl. 105; Berkeley, University of California, 1960, *Art from Ingres to Pollock*, p. 58; New York, 1961, no. 11, reprod.; Cambridge, Fogg Art Museum, and New York, Museum of Modern Art, 1965-67, *Memorial Exhibition: Works of Art from the Collection of Paul J. Sachs*, no. 43, reprod.

In 1796, Jeanne-Susanne Alliou, born in Paris in 1775, married Charles-Roche Hayard. Several years later, at some point between 1799 and 1806, the Hayards moved from Paris to Rome where Charles had a shop, at via dei due Macelli, no. 69, near the Piazza di Spagna, that sold artists' materials: "penelli, colori, carta vegatabile, tavolette d'avorio di ogni grandezza, ed ogni sorte d' attrezzi per Pittori" (Naef, *op. cit.,* p. 40). This portrait was probably drawn in the early months of 1810, before the arrival of Susanne's youngest child, Caroline, born in Rome, 17 July 1810 (No. 28).

After her husband's death in 1839, Mme. Hayard returned to Paris, where she died in 1854.

*Fogg Art Museum, Harvard University,*
*Bequest of Meta and Paul J. Sachs, 1965.298*

Graphite on white wove paper. 8¹⅜ x 6½ in. (224 x 165 mm.)*

Watermark: G. Jones | 1805.

Signed at the right center: *Ingres à | rome 1811*

CONDITION:      When the drawing was removed from an old mount the edges, which had been glued down, were slightly damaged. These have been mended, and a tear at the upper left has been repaired. The drawing has been bleached.

PROVENANCE:     Wildenstein to Grenville L. Winthrop, January, 1921.

REPRODUCTIONS: Lithographed by an anonymous artist.

BIBLIOGRAPHY:   Galichon, 1861, p. 360 (if it is not a reference to the Bonnat version); Delaborde, 1870, no. 355 (if it is not a reference to the Bonnat version); Blanc, 1870, p. 245 (a reference to the lithograph after the drawing); Jouin, 1888, p. 119 (if it is not a reference to either the Bonnat version or the frontal portrait in the collection of Mrs. Herbert N. Straus); Lapauze, 1901, p. 267 (a reference to the lithograph after the drawing); Mongan, 1944, p. 392; Alazard, 1950, p. 51; Ternois, 1959, p. 46; Naef, 1963, p. 66, reprod. p. 78.

EXHIBITIONS:    Paris, 1861 (or the Bonnat version).

There is a seemingly insoluble problem concerning this drawing and its history. A replica, alike in everything except minor details and a different placing of the signature and date, is in the Bonnat Collection, Bayonne. It is impossible to say which is the first, but clearly both are by Ingres. The one catalogued by Galichon and Delaborde remained in the Guillon Lethière family at least until 1870. Since the Bonnat version, like the Fogg one, is without a history, we do not know which one was listed by Galichon and Delaborde.

This drawing was made the year after Ingres left the Villa Medici. Four years later he drew the Director of the Villa Medici again (see No. 30).

*Fogg Art Museum, Harvard University,*
*Bequest of Grenville L. Winthrop, 1943.846*

Graphite and gray wash on white wove paper. 11$\frac{7}{16}$ x 16$\frac{5}{8}$ in. (291 x 422 mm.)

Inscribed on the curtain in the center background: *rideau*

The numerals "1" and "2" along the lower edge divide the composition into thirds horizontally. The design is squared for transfer.

CONDITION: The drawing was removed from the backing to which it had formerly been affixed. Although the surface was not disturbed, the paper was, as a result, thinned in many places. It has been mended at the lower edge. Scattered brown spots and a blue stain at the lower left have been minimized by bleaching.

PROVENANCE: Alphonse Kann to Paul J. Sachs.

BIBLIOGRAPHY: Delaborde, 1870, pp. 276-78; Lapauze, 1911, pp. 124-28; Mongan-Sachs, 1940, no. 700, fig. 371.

EXHIBITIONS: Providence, Rhode Island School of Design, 1937, *The Age of Canova*, no. 84, p. 14.

The *Virgil Reading the "Aeneid" to Augustus* of 1815, bequeathed by Ingres to the city of Toulouse, had been commissioned by General Miollis as a decoration for the Villa Aldobrandini (see No. 12). When he was Director of the French Academy in Rome, Ingres bought the canvas back from the Borghese family. It had been his lifelong intention to rework it, but he progressed no further than having his pupils begin to alter it. The canvas is nearly square in shape. The tall lamp by which Virgil reads his manuscript is a slender metal one. The central group is widely spaced, with Livia sitting nearer to Virgil than to Augustus. There is no figure of Marcellus.

When we catalogued this drawing in 1940 (Mongan-Sachs, no. 700) and listed other drawings connected with the composition, we noted its resemblance to the Brussels painting, said to have been painted in 1819. Further study has revealed that the figures in the Brussels painting are in precisely the same position as those in the right half of the Sachs drawing, although cut at the top and bottom. This fact suggests that at some point, a composition double the size of the Brussels painting once existed, probably even before the Toulouse version. In fact, the Brussels painting measures less than half the Toulouse version (Brussels, 54$\frac{3}{8}$ x 55$\frac{7}{8}$ in.; Toulouse, 119 x 128 in.). This thesis receives support from a tracing at Bayonne which repeats the Sachs drawing but with many details added (Giraudon, 13433), including the statue of Marcellus in the doorway, a figure not yet present here. The Sachs drawing shows that the exact center of the composition was the base of the statue of Marcellus, just above Octavia's knees.

In both the Sachs drawing and in the Bayonne drawing the group of Augustus, Livia and Octavia is closely knit, as it is in the Brussels painting. In short, we suggest that the Brussels painting is all that remains of a larger composition. In the Toulouse painting and in the later repetition, Livia is nearer to Virgil and the group is not as compact.

We did not note in our earlier discussion the fact, since noted by Schlenoff, that in the pose of Octavia there are reminiscences of Girodet's illustration for *Phaedre*, Act V, Scene vii, and that the pose of Livia owes much to Canova's portrait of Letizia Bonaparte (Madame Mère) as Agrippina, a statue made in Rome between 1805 and 1808.

*Fogg Art Museum, Harvard University,*
*Bequest of Meta and Paul J. Sachs, 1965.299*

Graphite and white chalk on brown wove paper, squared for transfer. 12⅞ x 9⅛ in. (316 x 250 mm.)

Signed at the lower right: *Ing*

Inscriptions, legible in part: At the lower left: ... *noirs;* on Livia's shoulder: *Livia* ... ; under the elbow of Augustus' raised arm: *reflet;* behind Augustus' neck: *moins de demi teinte* (?).

Turquoise stamp of the Ingres Sale at the lower right (L. 1477).

CONDITION: The brown paper has darkened as a result of exposure to light. A vertical crease and stains near the left edge indicate the point at which it was formerly glued down. The drawing is lightly foxed.

PROVENANCE: Presumably E. F. Haro (Ingres Sale, 1867); Reginald Davis, Paris; acquired by Grenville L. Winthrop, 1927.

BIBLIOGRAPHY: Mongan, 1944, p. 406.

In this drawing Ingres is suggesting, by the use of heightening in white on brown paper, the dramatic effect of night light which he had planned for his painting. As in the following drawing and the Brussels version, Livia is still close enough to Octavia to support the latter's head with her left hand. As we said earlier, the figure of Livia was obviously influenced by Canova's statue of Mme. Mère as Agrippina. In the early years of the century, Canova's Roman atelier was a place of pilgrimage for artists and the world of fashion. Madame de Staël in *Corinne,* which appeared in Rome in its first translation in 1808, described the lovers of her tale as visiting, at a late hour, the studio of Canova, "le plus grand sculpteur moderne ... comme il était tard ce fut aux flambeaux qu'ils se le firent montrer; et les statues gagnent beaucoup à cette manière d'être vues" (Schlenoff, 1956, p. 102). Ingres may have had a similar experience, one which would have affected him strongly.

*Fogg Art Museum, Harvard University,*
*Bequest of Grenville L. Winthrop, 1942.44b*

STUDY FOR THE HEAD OF OCTAVIA IN "VIRGIL READING THE 'AENEID' TO AUGUSTUS"    ca. 1812

Graphite and white chalk on brown wove paper. $6\frac{1}{16}$ x $8\frac{9}{16}$ in. (154 x 218 mm.) The rectangle is irregular.

Signed at the lower right: *Ing*

Turquoise stamp of the Ingres Sale at the lower right (L. 1477).

CONDITION: The white heightening has been partially effaced and, along the throat, retouched. Exposure to light has caused a general darkening of the design area, and an old mount has produced a rectangular stain along the edges of the paper.

PROVENANCE: Presumably E. F. Haro (Ingres Sale, 1867); Reginald Davis, Paris; acquired by Grenville L. Winthrop, 1927.

BIBLIOGRAPHY: Mongan, 1944, p. 406.

This beautiful and moving drawing is, like No. 21, connected with the composition laid out in No. 20. Even Livia's fingers are lightly indicated, as is the dramatic flickering light from the candelabra.

*Fogg Art Museum, Harvard University,*
*Bequest of Grenville L. Winthrop, 1942.44a*

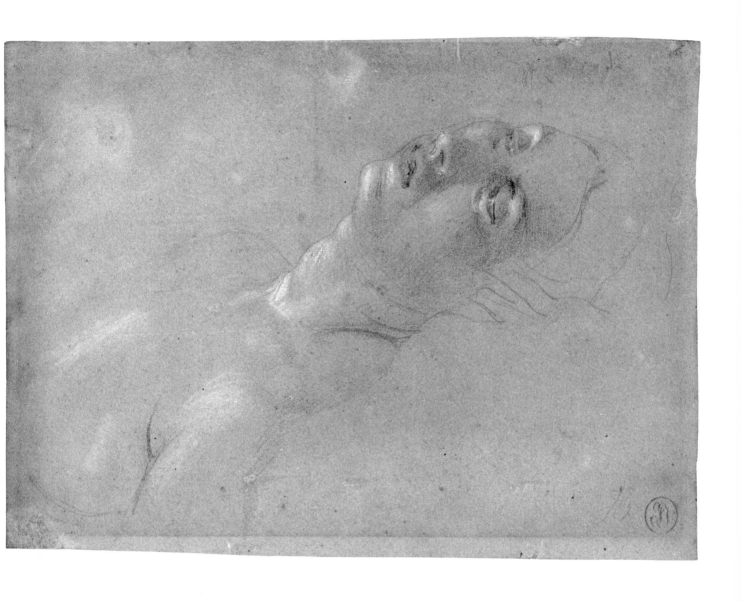

Hard graphite on cream-colored wove paper. 12⅜ x 9⅝ in. (314 x 244 mm.)

Signed at the lower right corner: *Ingres D.ᵛⁱᵗ a rome | 1812*

CONDITION:    Two large tears at the upper right have been mended. In the lower half, large areas of drawing were erased and altered by the artist.

PROVENANCE:    Maurice Delestre (Sale, Paris, Hôtel Drouot, 14 December 1936, no. 71); Vitale Bloch to Smith College, 1937.

REPRODUCTIONS: Soft-ground etching by Louise Girard, 1850.

BIBLIOGRAPHY:    Delaborde, 1870, no. 347, p. 303; Blanc, 1870, p. 245; Lapauze, 1901, p. 267; Lapauze, 1911, reprod. p. 124; Paul Marmottan, "Sur Achille Leclère," *Bulletin de la Société de l'histoire de l'art français,* 1921 Annual, Paris, 1922, p. 126; *Smith College Museum of Art Catalogue,* Northampton, 1937, p. 41, reprod. p. 129; "A New Ingres Drawing and a Bonnard Landscape," *Art News,* XXXVI, 11 December 1937, p. 17 reprod.; Jere Abbot, "A Drawing by J.-A.-D. Ingres," *Smith College Museum of Art Bulletin,* nos. 18-19, June, 1938, pp. 7-9, reprod. no. 2; H. R. Hitchcock, Jr., "A Note on A. Leclère," *Smith College Museum of Art Bulletin,* nos. 18-19, June, 1938, p. 10; Mongan, 1947, no. 4, reprod.; R. Huyghe and P. Jaccottet, *Le dessin français au XIXe siècle,* Lausanne, 1948, p. 173, reprod. p. 15; Shoolman and Slatkin, 1950, pl. 63; Alazard, 1950, p. 51; *Forty French Pictures in the Smith College Museum of Art,* Northampton, 1953, XXII-XXIII, reprod. no. 4; S. Lane Faison, Jr., *A Guide to New England Art Museums,* New York, 1958, p. 138, reprod.; Rosine Raoul, "The Taste for Drawings," *Apollo,* LXXXVII, July, 1962, reprod. p. 412.

EXHIBITIONS:    Springfield, etc., 1939-40, no. 46; San Francisco, 1947, no. 5 reprod.; New York, Knoedler, 1953, *Paintings and Drawings from the Smith College Collection,* no. 19; Rotterdam, Paris, New York, 1958-59, no. 96, pl. 128; Chicago, Art Club of Chicago, 1961, *Smith College Loan Exhibition,* no. 32; University of Minnesota, University Gallery, and New York, The Solomon R. Guggenheim Museum, 1962, *The Nineteenth Century: One Hundred Twenty-five Master Drawings,* no. 63.

Achille-François-René Leclère (1785-1853), at the left, and his colleague Jean-Louis Provost (1781-1850), at the right, were both natives of Paris. They studied under Charles Percier and continued their architectural training at the French Academy in Rome. Leclère, winner of the *Premier prix de Rome* for architecture in 1808, lived there between 1808 and 1814. Provost, a winner in 1811, arrived in Italy the following year. It was at this time that Ingres drew the two friends, reunited once again at the Villa Medici. A second portrait of Provost, alone, in a similar pose but with a much livelier expression, was executed one year later. It is now in the collection of Dr. and Mrs. Rudolf J. Heinemann, New York.

In his later career as an architect, Leclère was more successful than his friend Provost. He is still remembered today at the École des Beaux-Arts, Paris, where a prize carries his name.

*Smith College Museum of Art, Northampton*

Hard graphite on white wove paper. 10½ x 7¾ in. (267 x 198 mm.)*

Signed at the lower left: *Ingres a rome | 1813*

PROVENANCE: Mme. Jean-Baptiste-Auguste Vinchon to her daughter Mme. Charles-Jules Cormuau, née Thérèse-Victoire-Berthe Vinchon; her son, Charles-Jules Cormuau, to Charles-Victor Pardinel (d. 1921); François Coty (Sale, Paris, Charpentier Gallery, 30 November and 1 December 1936, no. 8, reprod.).

BIBLIOGRAPHY: Henry Lapauze, "Quelques oeuvres inédites de Ingres," *La Renaissance de l'art français,* December, 1922, p. 652, reprod.

The name of Madame de Senonnes is known to all lovers of Ingres from her superb painted portrait of 1814, now in the museum at Nantes (Wildenstein, 1954, no. 109, pl. 40). When Lapauze published this drawing in 1922 (*op. cit.*), he rejected the suggestion that it represented Madame de Senonnes, unconvinced by the label on the back which bore her name. At that time, however, he was unacquainted with the drawing's history. Until 1912, it had belonged to the descendants of Ingres' colleague Vinchon. When it was purchased from the family by the painter Charles-Victor Pardinel, it was called a portrait of Madame de Senonnes. There is little likelihood that the Vinchon family would have invented the title. Furthermore, a comparison of the drawing and the painting, taking into account the difference in pose and costume, leaves little doubt that the two represent the same sitter.

The familiar romantic story of Marie Marcoz' origin and life can be proved quite untrue. She was, in fact, not from Trastevere, but the daughter of a well-to-do merchant of Lyons. At nineteen she married a neighbor of suitable standing, Jean Talonsier. After the birth of a daughter in 1803, the couple went to Rome for her husband's business. In Rome, the marriage broke up and in 1809 they were divorced. The Vicomte de Senonnes, a noble of the ancien régime, a collector, draughtsman and student of antiquity, went to Rome in 1805 where in due course he met Ingres. In 1814 when Ingres painted Marie Marcoz, she was the mistress of Senonnes. They were married in Paris after the fall of the Empire when he became secretary-general of French museums and occupied an apartment in the Louvre. Later he was named *Secrétaire Général du Ministère de la Maison du Roi.* La Vicomtesse de Senonnes died in 1828 at the age of forty-five.

*Private Collection*

Ingres a rome
1813

Graphite on white wove paper.  10 x 7¾ in.  (254 x 197 mm.)*

Signed at the lower left: *Ingres—*

Red stamp of the E. F. Haro Collection at the lower right (L. 1241).

PROVENANCE:    E. F. Haro; Riant.

EXHIBITIONS:    Paris, Musée de l'Orangerie, 1956-57, *Exposition de la Collection Lehman de New York,* no. 140; Cincinnati, Cincinnati Art Museum, 1959, *The Lehman Collection,* no. 277; New York, 1961, no. 13, reprod.

During the course of his life, Ingres painted five versions of *Raphael and the Fornarina.* The earliest, which was signed and dated 1813 and which belonged to the museum in Riga, was lost at the time of the German invasion in 1941. Unfortunately we have not been able to find a reproduction of that painting. A year later Ingres repeated the subject in a version now in the Fogg Museum. The Fogg painting was shown in the Salon of 1814.

This drawing is more closely related to the Fogg variant than to the three subsequent versions, one sold in New York in 1948 (Wildenstein, no. 89), one in a New York private collection assigned to 1840 (Wildenstein, no. 231), and the last, on which Ingres was still working in 1860 (Wildenstein, no. 297), now in a French private collection. In the latter three the Fornarina has both hands resting on Raphael's left shoulder.

When he made this drawing Ingres was still struggling to find a satisfactory position for the arms. He has tried the left arm in three positions and sketched the left hand twice, at the left hand corner in the position adopted in the Fogg painting. In the soft touch of the pencil on the paper and in the conception of form, the study is akin to other early Roman figure drawings.

It is tempting to see in the model's calm gaze and slightly amused look a likeness to Madeleine Chapelle, Ingres' bride of that year.

An accurate replica of the drawing exists, possibly made by a pupil while the Lehman drawing was still in Ingres' studio (Fogg Art Museum, no. 1942.66). A variant, a finished design for a group never painted but which repeats the figures in the position of the Fogg painting, is in the Louvre. It is dated 1825 on the reverse.

*Robert Lehman, New York*

Hard graphite on cream-colored wove paper. 11½ x 8⅛ in. (292 x 206 mm.)

Signed at the right: *Ingres.* | *1814.*

PROVENANCE:    Henry Lapauze (Sale, Paris, Hôtel Drouot, 21 June 1929, no. 19, reprod. opp. p. 12); Wildenstein, New York, to Mrs. Grace Rainey Rogers, 1940.

BIBLIOGRAPHY:    *Beaux-Arts,* VII, no. 5, 15 July 1929, reprod. p. 15; Louise Burroughs, "Drawings by Ingres," *The Metropolitan Museum of Art Bulletin,* IV, February, 1946, reprod. p. 158; Mongan, 1947, no. 6, reprod.; E. Bénézit, *Dictionnaire critique et documentaire des peintres,* Paris, 1952, V, frontispiece.

The identity of the sitter is unknown, but Dr. Naef has suggested that the drawing is a pendant to the portrait of an unknown man now in the Boymans-van Beuningen Museum, Rotterdam, a suggestion we find convincing. The two drawings were formerly in the Lapauze Collection. In the sale of that collection (*op. cit.*) they were numbered 18 and 19; the measurements given for the two were identical. If considered as a pair, they face each other, as do other Ingres pairs. The quiet, reflective expression of the lovely lady offers an interesting contrast to the lively, appraising look of the alert and engaging gentleman. The quality of drawing in both is superb.

*Metropolitan Museum of Art,*
*Bequest of Grace Rainey Rogers, 1943*

Graphite on white wove paper. 8⅜ x 6⁹⁄₁₆ in. (214 x 167 mm.)*

Watermark: J. Whatman (Heawood, no. 1849).

Brown stamp of the François Flameng Collection at the lower right (L. 991).

CONDITION:     With the exception of a slight vertical fold to the right of the central axis, the paper is in excellent condition. The drawing has been bleached.

PROVENANCE:     François Flameng (Sale, Paris, Georges Petit Gallery, 26-27 May 1919, no. 118).

BIBLIOGRAPHY:     Lapauze, 1911, p. 138, reprod.; Charles Saunier, "Collection François Flameng," *Les Arts,* no. 167, 1918, p. 24, reprod.; Bryson Burroughs, "Recent Accessions, Drawings by Ingres," *Bulletin of the Metropolitan Museum of Art,* xiv, November, 1919, p. 246, reprod. p. 229; Zabel, 1930, p. 382, reprod. p. 381, no. 19.

EXHIBITIONS:     Paris, 1911, no. 89; Springfield, etc., 1939-40, no. 39; San Francisco, 1947, no. 7.

The sitter has never been identified, in spite of his extraordinary visage and his personal distinction. Ingres has seen him as full of irony and humor.

*The Metropolitan Museum of Art,*
*Rogers Fund, 1919*

Ingres. 1814

Graphite on white wove paper. 11½ x 8⅝ in. (292 x 220 mm.)

Signed at the lower left: *Ingres | a | Monsieur Hayard | rome 1815*

CONDITION:     Two small spots at the upper left were mended and later bleached. When the paper was removed from a former support it suffered minor thinning along the back of the right side.

PROVENANCE:    Charles Hayard (d. 1839) to Mme. Charles Hayard (d. 1854); to her daughter, Mme. Félix Duban (d. 1881); to her sister, Mme. Frédéric Flachéron (d. 1894); to her son, Félix Flachéron (d. 1927); Scott and Fowles, New York, to Grenville L. Winthrop, December, 1922.

BIBLIOGRAPHY:  Galichon, 1861, p. 359; Delaborde, 1870, p. 300, no. 322; Blanc, 1870, p. 237; Duplessis, 1896, no. 13, reprod., photogravure by Charreyre; Lapauze, 1901, p. 266, reprod. after the photogravure of Charreyre; Lapauze, 1911, reprod. p. 155; Charles Saunier, "Exposition Ingres," *Les Arts,* x, July, 1911, reprod. p. 12; Louis Hourticq, *Ingres,* Paris, 1928, pl. 45; Mongan, 1944, p. 293, reprod.; Ternois, 1959, p. 52, reprod.; Hans Naef, "Ingres et la Famille Hayard," *Gazette des Beaux-Arts,* LXVII, January, 1966, pp. 37-50.

EXHIBITIONS:   Paris, 1861, no. 61; Paris, 1867, no. 353.

Caroline was born in Rome in July, 1810 (see No. 18). In 1838, she married a young Belgian painter, Edmond Duvivier, who died the year after their marriage (26 September 1839). Ingres had been a witness at the wedding. He drew her likeness again in 1841 (Naef, *op. cit.,* fig. 8, p. 49) when he was director of the French Academy in Rome. A year later she remarried, this time to a sculptor, Frédéric Flachéron.

This drawing, which shows Caroline at the age of five with her mother, was the companion piece to a drawing which Ingres made of her father with her elder sister Marguerite, a drawing which belonged to the late César de Hauke (Naef, *op. cit.,* fig. 5, p. 44).

*Fogg Art Museum, Harvard University,*
*Bequest of Grenville L. Winthrop, 1943.848*

Ingres
a
Monsieur Bujac
Rome 1815

Graphite on white wove paper.  9½ x 6⅜ in.  (242 x 162 mm.)*

Signed at the upper left: *Ingres Del.*; dated at the upper right: *rome 1815*; calligraphic inscription with pen and ink at upper center: *À L'amitié*.

PROVENANCE:    Baron Vitta (perhaps bequeathed to him by the sitter's son Fiorillo-Henri-Edmond Four-
               nier, together with the portrait of M. de Nogent); César M. de Hauke to John S. Thacher,
               ca. 1952.

BIBLIOGRAPHY:  Hans Naef, "Notes on Ingres Drawings I, The Engraver Fournier," *The Art Quarterly*,
               xx, Summer, 1957, pp. 183-87, reprod. p. 185.

EXHIBITIONS:   Nice, Palais des Arts, 1931, *Ingres*, no. 15; New Haven, Yale University Art Gallery, 1956,
               *Pictures Collected by Yale Alumni*, no. 207.

Jean-Georges-Joseph Fournier was an engraver of whom little is known. He had a son, Fiorillo-Henri-Edmond Fournier, whose memoirs unfortunately tell us almost nothing of his father. In volume II he writes, near the beginning, that he was born in Naples and that his father's house was situated "à mi-coteau entre Capodimonte et St. Elme ... mon père aimait les fleurs et j'ai vécu au milieu d'elles les premières années de mon enfance." The engraver died before 1884.

J. Guiffrey in the preface of the Vitta Sale Catalogue (15 March 1935) writes, "Une note de Ingres lui-même nous apprend qu'il approvait pour lui (Monsieur Nogent) une profonde amitié, que partageait le graveur Fournier. Les trois amis se rencontrent souvent à Rome, et aux environs, et se séjourent même ensembles à Naples. L'histoire du portrait (Monsieur de Nogent, Fogg Art Museum) est dénouée de tout complication. Monsieur de Nogent lega son portrait à Fournier, son camarade de Rome, et le fils de celui-ci, Fiorillo Fournier, le laisse à sa mort à son ami le Baron Joseph Vitta" (from whose collection the Thacher drawing also comes). If, in truth, Fournier was an engraver, he moved in high social circles, for his son in his memoirs writes that "grace aux relations de ma famille, Monsieur Guizot, Ministre des affaires étrangères, recommandat chaudement mon père à Monsieur le Duc de Montebello, notre ambassadeur à la cour des Deux Siciles."

In the light of Guiffrey's statement the inscription "À L'amitié" on this very handsome drawing assumes a special interest.

*John S. Thacher, Washington, D. C.*

À L'amitié

Graphite. 10¹¹⁄₁₆ x 8⁵⁄₁₆ in. (271 x 211 mm.)

Inscribed at the lower right: *M^{de} Ingres* | *a Mad^{lle} Lescot*. A signature, now erased, is still legible beneath the dedication: *Ingres rome 1815.*

PROVENANCE:     Hortense Haudebourt-Lescot; Adrien Fauchier-Magnan; Wildenstein, Paris, to Mr. and Mrs. Herbert N. Straus, 1930.

BIBLIOGRAPHY:     Jouin, 1888, p. 119 (if it is not a reference to the profile portrait in Bayonne or the one in the Fogg Art Museum); Zabel, 1930, reprod. p. 379; Aline B. Louchheim, "The Great Tradition of French Drawing from Ingres to Picasso in American Collections," *Art News Annual,* XLIII, 1944, p. 129; Mongan, 1947, no. 9.

EXHIBITIONS:     Paris, Palais des Beaux-Arts, 1913, *David et ses élèves,* no. 332, reprod. opp. p. 80; Paris, 1921, no. 64; Buffalo, Albright Art Gallery, 1935, *Master Drawings,* no. 95; Springfield, etc., 1939-40, no. 47; New York, 1961, no. 6, reprod.

Guillaume Guillon Lethière was born at St. Ann, Guadaloupe, in 1760, the natural son of Pierre Guillon, agent of the King at Guadeloupe. As Guillaume was the third child of Guillon, he was called Letiers, which he later changed to Lethière. He went to France while quite young, became a pupil of David, and won a second place *prix de Rome* in 1784. In June, 1807, he was appointed director of the French Academy in Rome after Suvée's sudden death, but only took up his directorship there in October of the same year. Ingres knew him when he was a pensioner at the Academy and remained on the best of terms with Guillon Lethière and his family after 1810 when he left to have his own quarters in Rome.

Guillon Lethière was Lucien Bonaparte's agent, helping the latter with the acquisition of antiquities. It was presumably Guillaume Lethière who introduced Ingres to Lucien. From this meeting came not only the portrait of Lucien himself (No. 11), but also Ingres' most ambitious portrait group, that of Lucien's family (No. 33). Alexander Dumas wrote, "Monsieur Lethière était à la fois un beau talent, un bon coeur et un charmant esprit" (*Mémoires,* XI, Brussels, 1852, p. 139). He died in Paris in 1832. The Fogg Museum possesses a large drawing by him, the Worcester Art Museum a charming painted portrait of a young woman. There is a profile pen portrait of Guillon Lethière by David d'Angers, identified recently by Dr. Naef, at the Clark Institute, Williamstown.

Mrs. Straus' drawing is dedicated to Hortense Lescot who became a famous painter under the name of Madame Haudebourt-Lescot. An orphan and a pupil of Guillon Lethière, she followed him to Rome to the consternation of some of the villa's inhabitants (see H. Lapauze, *Histoire de l'Académie de France à Rome,* chapter on the directorship of Guillon Lethière).

*Mrs. Herbert N. Straus, New York*

M. de Ingres
a Mad.lle Lescot

Hard and soft graphite on white wove paper. 11⅛ x 8¾ in. (300 x 222 mm.)

Stamp of the Metropolitan Museum of Art on the verso at the lower left.

CONDITION: The paper, once discolored by an earlier mount of wood pulp board, has been restored to approximately its original color by bleaching.

PROVENANCE: Marquis de Biron (not in sale of 1914); Wildenstein to Mrs. Grace Rainey Rogers, 1940.

BIBLIOGRAPHY: Lapauze, 1921, reprod. p. 229; Louise Burroughs, "Drawings by Ingres," *The Metropolitan Museum of Art Bulletin,* IV, February, 1946, reprod. p. 159; Ternois, 1959, above no. 63; Naef, 1963, p. 76, pl. 7.

EXHIBITIONS: Paris, 1921, no. 66, reprod.; New York, 1961, no. 18, reprod.

Rosina Meli, a young Roman, was the second wife of Guillon Lethière's son, Alexandre. Their daughter was born in Rome, 14 August 1814, and christened Letizia, undoubtedly after Madame Mère. Hortense Lescot (see No. 30) was the baby's godmother. Since the child can be little more than a year old, the drawing must have been made in 1815. Ingres has responded here to feminine charm, as he did from youth to his last years. The young mother, with her lovely oval face, her eyebrows gently arching above her almost oriental eyes, clearly appealed to the artist, as did the baby girl. Mother and child seem just about to smile in response to some sally from their observer, but for the instant they are magically and timelessly still. Life was not generous to the young woman. She died two years later. We do not know from what cause.

*Metropolitan Museum of Art,*
*Bequest of Grace Rainey Rogers, 1943*

PORTRAIT OF ALEXANDRE LETHIÈRE, HIS WIFE ROSINA AND THEIR DAUGHTER LETIZIA

Graphite on white wove paper. 10⅞ x 8⅞ in. (278 x 221 mm.)

Signed at the lower left: *Ingres- à | Monsieur Lethière. | rome 1815*

CONDITION: The drawing is exceptionally well preserved. It has suffered only slight foxing and minimal discoloration as a result of age and exposure to light.

PROVENANCE: The sitters' son Charles Lethière (d. 1889) to his widow Mme. Clémence Lethière; Bestigui; Wildenstein to the Museum of Fine Arts, Boston, 1926.

BIBLIOGRAPHY: Charles Blanc, "Le Salon des Arts-Unis," *Gazette des Beaux-Arts,* IX, February, 1861, p. 191; Henri Delaborde, "Les dessins de M. Ingres au Salon des Arts-Unis," *Gazette des Beaux-Arts,* IX, March, 1861, p. 267; Galichon, 1861, p. 360; Delaborde, 1870, no. 354; Jules Momméja, *Collection Ingres au Musée de Montauban, Inventaire général des richesses d'art de la France,* Paris, 1905, VII, p. 54; Lapauze, 1921, reprod. p. 218; "A Drawing by Ingres," *Bulletin of the Museum of Fine Arts,* XXIV, June, 1926, pp. 38-39, reprod.; Zabel, 1930, p. 381, reprod.; Regina Shoolman and Charles E. Slatkin, *The Enjoyment of Art in America,* Philadelphia and New York, 1942, p. 547, fig. 507; Bryan Holme, *Master Drawings,* New York and London, 1944, p. 13, pl. 92; Mongan, 1947, no. 8, reprod.; Hans Tietze, *European Master Drawings in the United States,* New York, 1947, no. 124, reprod.; Shoolman and Slatkin, 1950, p. 114, pl. 64; Alazard, 1950, p. 63, pl. XXXI; Ternois, 1959, above no. 63; Naef, 1963, pp. 75-76, fig. 5.

EXHIBITIONS: Paris, 1861; Cambridge, 1934, no. 43; Buffalo, Albright Art Gallery, 1935, *Master Drawings,* no. 94; San Francisco, Golden Gate International Exposition, 1940, *Master Drawings,* no. 56; Worcester, Worcester Art Museum, 1951-52, *The Practice of Drawing,* no. 39; Montreal, Montreal Museum of Fine Arts, 1953, *Five Centuries of Drawings,* no. 184, reprod.; Paris, Musée de l'Orangerie, 1955, *David à Toulouse-Lautrec,* no. 81, pl. 4; New York, 1961, no. 17, reprod.

Alexandre Lethière was a naval officer who had served with distinction in naval battles in the West Indies during the War of 1812. He was taken prisoner by the English. After his liberation he was appointed administrator of the excise tax on tobacco in Rome, where he met and married his second wife, Rosina Meli. After the collapse of the Empire, he returned to Paris where he died in 1827, his health undermined, it is said, by his treatment in the English prison.

A separate drawing of him in the Bonnat Collection, Bayonne, and the Metropolitan drawing of Rosina and their daughter (No. 31) seem complete in themselves. Ingres then combined the figures into a single group. The method by which he proceeded is made clear in a tracing at Montauban which shows the young parents with the child still at her mother's knee. In the Boston drawing he has improved the composition by placing the child on her mother's lap, the focal point of the composition.

*The Museum of Fine Arts, Boston*

Ingres. à
Monsieur Lethière
Rome 1815

Graphite on white wove paper. 16¼ x 20⅛ in. (412 x 529 mm.)

Watermark: J WHATMAN | 1813.

Signed at the lower right: *J. Ingres. Del (Rom,* erased) | *Rome 1815*

CONDITION:      Exposure to light has slightly discolored the paper.

PROVENANCE:      Lucien Bonaparte (d. 1840) to his widow, née Alexandrine Jacob de Bleschamps; stolen before 1841; bought by the painter Charles de Chatillon for Mme. Lucien Bonaparte at an unknown Sale, Paris, ca. 1841; Countess Zeffirina Faino, née Luciana Valentini di Laviano, granddaughter and sole heir of Mme. Bonaparte, to her nephew, Count Giuseppe Primoli, 1903; Georges Bernheim Gallery, Paris, 1918; Hermann Heilbuth, Denmark; Danske Landmansbank, Copenhagen; Gorm Rasmussen, Sølyst near Copenhagen to Jacques Seligman, New York, 1936; to Grenville L. Winthrop, 1936.

BIBLIOGRAPHY:      Edmond Saglio, "Un nouveau tableau de M. Ingres, Liste complète de ses oeuvres," *La Correspondance littéraire,* February, 1857; Delaborde, 1870, no. 264; Guida di Perugia, third edition, 1878, p. 97; Lapauze, 1901, p. 248; Lapauze, 1903, p. 17, fn. 1; Lapauze, 1911, pp. 180-82; Lapauze, "La famille Lucien Bonaparte," *La Renaissance de l'art français,* March, 1918, pp. 12-15, reprod. p. 14; Paul Fleuriot de Langle, "Monsieur Ingres et la princesse de Canino," *La Revue de France,* 1 July 1939, pp. 34-43; Paul Fleuriot de Langle, *Alexandrine Lucien Bonaparte, princesse de Canino,* Paris, 1939, p. 155, fn. p. 157, reprod. opp. p. 296; Walter Pach, *Ingres,* New York, 1939, pp. 41 ff., pp. 248 ff., p. 25, reprod. opp. p. 103; Mongan, 1944, pp. 393-95, reprod. p. 393; Mongan, 1947, no. 10 reprod.; Agnes Mongan, *One Hundred Master Drawings,* Cambridge, 1949, p. 132, reprod.; Alazard, 1950, p. 64, pl. XXIX; Shoolman and Slatkin, 1950, p. 120, pl. 67; Carlo Pietrangeli, *Il Museo Napoleonico,* Rome, 1950, p. 101; Carlo Pietrangeli, "Un autografo di Ingres nel Museo Napoleonico," *Bolletino dei Musei communali di Roma,* II, nos. 3-4, 1955, pp. 47-51, reprod. p. 49; Ternois, 1959, cited under no. 13; Else Kai Sass, "Ingres Drawing of the Family of Lucien Bonaparte," *Burlington Magazine,* CII, January, 1960, pp. 19-21, fig. 26; Hans Naef, "Vier Ingres-Zeichnungen," *Pantheon,* VIII, no. 1, 1960, pp. 35 ff., reprod. p. 36; Germain Seligman, *Merchants of Art: 1880-1960, Eighty Years of Professional Collecting,* New York, 1961, p. 149, pl. 44; René Gimpel, *Journal d'un collectionneur marchand de tableaux,* Paris, 1963, p. 64 (entry for 10 August 1918); Else Kai Sass, *Thorvaldsens Portraetbuster,* Copenhagen, 1963, I, pp. 400, 406, reprod. p. 399.

The drawing is the largest and most ambitious of all Ingres' portrait drawings. Assembled around Alexandrine de Bleschamps, Lucien's second wife, are their various children, his daughter Charlotte by his first wife, Caroline Boyer, and Alexandrine's eldest daughter by her first marriage. Alexandrine was awaiting the birth of another child, born in September 1815. The drawing was made during the Hundred Days (20 March-28 June) when Lucien, putting aside his disagreements with his brother, went to join him at Waterloo. He is represented by Marin's portrait bust in the background. Mme. Mère, the matriarch of that extraordinary family, is represented by Canova's bust of her dressed as Agrippina.

There is universal agreement in the identification of only five of the sitters: Alexandrine herself and the three little boys surrounding her, Paul-Marie, on the floor at her feet (b. 1809); Louis-

Lucien, at his mother's knee (b. 1813); and Charles-Lucien, with his left arm at the back of his mother's chair (b. 1803). Concerning the identification of the others, Lapauze and Professor Else Kai Sass of Copenhagen do not agree. Part of the difficulty revolves around the fact that Charlotte (or Carlotta) was absent from Rome during the spring of 1815. She did not return to Rome until 1816. Lapauze identifies the girl with the lyre at the left as Anna Jouberthon (b. 1800) Alexandrine's daughter by her first marriage and the girl next to her on the stool as Christine. The three at the right, from left to right, are Jeanne, Letizia and Charlotte. For Professor Kai Sass, they are from left to right: Charlotte, Jeanne, Anna, Letizia and Christine, better known as Christine-Egypt.

When Magimel was planning his publication in 1850, Ingres wrote to Alexandrine, then residing at Canino, and asked to borrow the drawing. He explained why and said that he would like to add Lucien's portrait to the composition. The drawing was not sent. Everyone acquainted with the story was relieved that the drawing did not again come into Ingres' hands, feeling that in changing it he might have ruined it. Ingres was, in writing for the drawing, obviously conscious of the fact that historically, as well as artistically, this drawing was one of his greatest achievements. In his list of his own works (Lapauze, 1901, p. 248, Cahier x), it is the only portrait drawing done in Rome that he records. A further proof of the importance he attached to it, is that he wanted to include it in the Magimel book which reproduced, in addition to his best paintings, only his closest friends and relatives, with the single exception of Pressigny.

No preparatory drawings for this large, complex group are known. If Ingres followed the same procedure that he used when preparing the Alexandre Lethière family group (Nos. 31 and 32), he may have sketched them separately or in small groups, later uniting them in this single composition. His willingness to add Lucien later suggests such a procedure.

*Fogg Art Museum, Harvard University,*
*Bequest of Grenville L. Winthrop, 1943.837*

PORTRAIT OF FRAU REINHOLD, AND HER DAUGHTERS, SUSETTE-MARIE AND MARIE-AUGUSTE-FRIEDERIKE

Graphite. 12⅛ x 9⅜ in. (187 x 164 mm.) Irregular.

Signed at the lower right: *Ingres Del. Rome 1815*

CONDITION: The paper has been removed from the tablet around which it was originally stretched. As a result, the edges of the drawing are extraordinarily ragged. (See Technical Appendix.)

PROVENANCE: Johann Gotthard Reinhold (d. 1838) and his wife, née Minna Ritter (d. 1846); their daughter Frau Louis Köster, née Marie-Auguste-Friederike Ritter (d. 1873); Frederick Keppel & Co., New York, to an anonymous New York collector, 1931.

BIBLIOGRAPHY: K. A. Varnhagen von Ense, *Tagebücher,* Zurich, 1865, VII, p. 220, entry for 17 June 1850; Hans Naef, "Zwei unveröffentlichte Ingres-Zeichnungen," *Schweizer Monatshefte,* March, 1956, pp. 649-54; Hans Naef, "Ein unveröffentlichtes Meisterwerk von Ingres in Staedelschen Kunstinstitut," *Die Weltkunst,* 15 February 1958, p. 9.

When this handsome drawing, which has never before been reproduced, first came to our attention many years ago, it was said to represent the wife of the Dutch Ambassador with two children. The drawing is dated Rome, 1815. In that year the Dutch Ambassador in Rome was a highly cultivated man of sterling character named Johann Gotthard Reinhold who had married, 16 March 1808, in Hamburg, Sophie-Amalie-Dorothea-Wilhelmina ("Minna") Ritter (born at Niemburg-am-Weser, ca. 1782). They had two children, Susette-Marie born on Christmas Eve, 1808, and Marie-Auguste-Friederike, born 2 March 1810 in Berlin. The age of these two daughters corresponds exactly to that of the two children in the drawing. The elder died in Rome in 1821, at the age of thirteen; in 1841 the younger married a merchant, Louis Köster, in Hamburg. It was at the pious instigation of Frau Köster that Vornhagen von Ense published two books of poetry (Leipzig, 1853) by her father, a contemporary and schoolmate of Schiller for whom he maintained a life-long veneration. Among his verses are some touching poems in which we meet again the figures in the drawing.

Group portraits by Ingres are rare. The others in the present exhibition are all of French families. One need only compare them with this mother and her two children to see that, even without a title, one might have guessed that this family was not French.

*Private Collection, New York*

Graphite on white wove paper. 15½ x 11½ in. (394 x 292 mm.)

Signed at the lower left: *Ingres fec. Roma 1815*

PROVENANCE:    In the family of the sitter until 1952; Edward Speelman, London; Otto Wertheimer, Paris, to the City Art Museum of St. Louis, 1952.

REPRODUCTIONS: Engraved by J. H. Wiffen, 1824 (a detail, reversed).

BIBLIOGRAPHY:    Hans Naef, "A Recently Discovered Drawing by Ingres," *Graphis,* VIII, Zurich, 1952, pp. 438-40, reprod. p. 439; William M. Eisendrath, "A Drawing by Ingres," *Bulletin of The City Art Museum of St. Louis,* XXXVII, St. Louis, 1953, pp. 14-16, reprod. p. 13; Helen Comstock, "An English Portrait by Ingres," *Connoisseur,* CXXXII, August, 1953, p. 69, reprod.; *Art News Annual,* XXIII, New York, 1954, reprod. p. 189; Hans Naef, "Ingres' Portrait Drawings of English Sitters in Rome," *Burlington Magazine,* XCVIII, December, 1956, p. 428, reprod. p. 433.

EXHIBITIONS:    Rotterdam, Paris, New York, 1958-59, no. 130, pl. 94; Newark, Newark Museum, 1960, *Old Master Drawings,* no. 61, reprod.

John Russell, sixth Duke of Bedford, lived from 1766-1839. He was a Privy Councillor, a member of Parliament from 1788-1802, and the Lord Lieutenant of Ireland in 1806. He retired from public life in 1807. One of England's great landowners, he was deeply interested in agriculture and questions of nutrition. From 1803-15, he was in Italy where he acquired an important collection of sculpture and painting, still conserved in part at Woburn Abbey.

Ingres also drew the portrait of his daughter-in-law, Elizabeth Ann Rawdon, later Lady Russell, a celebrated beauty who was as learned and intelligent as she was lovely. Her pencil portrait is known through a copy which still belongs to the family (Naef, *op. cit.*).

*City Art Museum of St. Louis*

PORTRAIT OF MRS. VESEY AND HER DAUGHTER ELIZABETH VESEY, LATER 1816
LADY COLTHURST

Graphite on white wove paper. 11¾ x 8¹⁸⁄₁₆ in. (299 x 224 mm.)

Signed at the lower right: *Ingres Del.* | *Rome* | *1816*

CONDITION: Vertical bands of discoloration along both the right and left edges, approximately 1⅜ in. wide, and narrower strips at the top and bottom suggest that the drawing was originally mounted on a wood stretcher.

PROVENANCE: Colonel and Mrs. George Vesey, Lucan House, Dublin; to Lady Colthurst, née Elizabeth Vesey, wife of Sir Nicholas Conway Colthurst; to her daughters, Ann Colthurst and Mrs. Bruce; Wildenstein, Paris, to Grenville L. Winthrop, November, 1931.

BIBLIOGRAPHY: William Rothenstein, *Men and Memories,* London, 1934, I, p. 103; *Beaux-Arts,* Paris, 30 March 1934, p. 2, reprod.; Ford, 1939, pp. 9 ff., pl. II B; Mongan, 1944, p. 397, fig. 5; Mongan, 1947, no. 11, reprod.; Alazard, 1950, p. 63.

EXHIBITIONS: London, Burlington House, 1907, *Old Masters,* no. 242; London, Burlington Fine Arts Club, 1917, *Drawings by Deceased Masters,* no. 18.

Emily Latouche, daughter of a French Huguenot family established in Ireland at the time of the Revocation of the Edict of Nantes, married Colonel George Vesey in November, 1790. Their only child, Elizabeth, is represented with her mother in this portrait of 1816, three years before her marriage to Sir Nicholas Conway Colthurst. The drawing remained with her descendants (she had four sons and a daughter) until well into the twentieth century. How Mrs. Vesey and her daughter, obviously on the Grand Tour after Waterloo, happened to sit for Ingres is not known.

*Fogg Art Museum, Harvard University,*
*Bequest of Grenville L. Winthrop, 1943.854*

Graphite on white wove paper. 10¼ x 8¼ in. (261 x 210 mm.)

Signed at the lower left: *J Ingres. Del Rome 1816*

PROVENANCE: Charles Badham (d. 1845); Badham family; C. Badham Jackson (Sale, London, Sotheby, 12 December 1928, no. 145, reprod.) to Dr. Borenius; Wildenstein, to Jesse I. Straus, 1929.

BIBLIOGRAPHY: Zabel, 1930, p. 378, reprod.; Jean Cassou, "Ingres et ses contradictions," *Gazette des Beaux-Arts,* XI, March, 1934, fig. 15, p. 157; Ford, 1939, pp. 8 ff., pl. III c; Naef, 1960, p. 27, reprod. fig. 52.

EXHIBITIONS: New York, 1961, no. 22, reprod.

In 1815 the Badhams, who lived in the Via Gregoriana, 25, were close neighbors of Ingres who lived at no. 34 of the same street. Charles Badham, a distinguished physician, was also a gifted Latinist and a passionate traveler. Between 1815-17, he traveled in the lesser known regions of Southern Italy and throughout Greece, leaving his wife and children in Rome.

His wife, born Margaret Campbell, was a noted beauty, a first cousin of the poet Thomas Campbell who seems to have sued for her hand unsuccessfully. She was thirty-five years of age when Ingres drew her, seated at the head of the Via Gregoriana, with the Villa Medici and the obelisk at the top of the Spanish Steps in the background.

*Mrs. Jesse I. Straus, New York*

Ingres. Del Roma 1816

Hard and soft graphite on cream-colored wove paper, affixed to a secondary support of heavy white paper. 8⅜ x 6¾ in. (219 x 172 mm.)*

Signed at the lower left: *Ingres fecit | roma | 1816* (over an earlier signature, *Ingres del,* which had been erased).

CONDITION:    Presumably the drawing was formerly stretched over a wood pulp board. At the time it was removed from this mount, the edges were seriously damaged.

PROVENANCE:    Unknown English collection; Henry Lapauze (Sale, Paris, Hôtel Drouot, 21 June 1929, no. 33, reprod. opp. p. 20); Knoedler, New York, to Mrs. Grace Rainey Rogers, 1931.

BIBLIOGRAPHY:    Henry Lapauze, "Un portrait inconnu de Ingres, Lady Cavendish-Bentinck," *La Renaissance de l'art français,* 2° Année, no. 1, January, 1919, pp. 8-10, reprod.; Ford, 1939, p. 7; Alazard, 1950, p. 62, pl. XXXIII.

EXHIBITIONS:    San Francisco, 1947, no. 8.

The identity of the sitter is problematic. She is presumed to be Mary Acheson, daughter of the first Earl of Gosford. In 1803, Lady Mary married William Henry Cavendish-Bentinck, son of the third Duke of Portland. A securely documented double portrait of her with her husband, also dated "Rome, 1816," is now preserved in the Musée Bonnat, Bayonne. Its resemblance to the Metropolitan's drawing is, however, suggestive rather than conclusive evidence in support of the identification. A second drawing, sold in England at approximately the same time as the Metropolitan portrait, and also presumed to represent Lady Mary, is now in the collection of the Rijksmuseum, Amsterdam. The similarity between this drawing and the portrait from the Rogers Collection is striking, lending credence to the latter's traditional title.

Although little is known about Lady Mary, her husband (1774-1839) had a varied and distinguished career. He was governor of Madras from 1803-07, a major general in Portugal in 1808, and commander in chief of the British forces in Sicily in 1811. The three portraits by Ingres were presumably made at the close of the war, when the Cavendish-Bentincks spent some time in Rome.

*The Metropolitan Museum of Art,
Bequest of Grace Rainey Rogers, 1943*

Ingres offecit
roma
1816

Graphite. 12 x 8½ in. (305 x 215 mm.)

Signed at the lower right: *Ingres. Del à | rome 1817*

PROVENANCE:    Sir Fleetwood Broughton Reynolds Pellew (d. 1861); presumably to his only child Lady
Walpole (Horatio William), née Harriet Bettina Frances Pellew; Georges Renand, Paris;
Paul Rosenberg, New York, to Mrs. Mark C. Steinberg, ca. 1956.

BIBLIOGRAPHY:  Hans Naef, "Ingres' Portrait Drawings of English Sitters in Rome," *Burlington Magazine*,
XCVIII, December, 1956, p. 428, reprod. p. 430; William N. Eisendrath, Jr., "Paintings and
Sculpture in the Collection of Mrs. Mark C. Steinberg," *Connoisseur*, CLIV, December,
1963, p. 267, reprod. p. 264.

EXHIBITIONS:   Paris, André Seligman Gallery, 1936, *Portraits Français de 1400 à 1900*, no. 129; Paris,
Marcel Guiot Gallery, 1937, *Le portrait dessiné au XIXᵉ siècle*, no. 13, reprod.

Sir Fleetwood was born 13 December 1789, the second son of the first Viscount Exmouth, a naval
hero of the Napoleonic Wars. His career, like his father's, was a naval one. His flagship was on
Mediterranean duty when the crew mutinied and the ship was ordered home. Pellew's harshness
had, it was said, goaded the men to rebel. The charges were quashed, and in June, 1815, he was
nominated a Commander of the Bath. From August 1818 to 1822, he was in command of the *Révo-
lutionnaire*. Again, after his appointment in 1832 on the East India and China stations, he seems to
have been too harsh and cruel to his men. Word reached England and he was recalled for "a la-
mentable lack of judgment." He was promoted to the rank of Admiral but given no further service.
He died in Marseilles in 1861 and was buried in the Protestant cemetery in Florence.

He had married in 1816, Harriet, the only daughter of Sir Geoffrey Webster. The drawing was
undoubtedly made when they were on their wedding journey. There is a portrait drawing of Lady
Pellew made in Rome in the same year (Private Collection, Paris).

*Mrs. Mark C. Steinberg, St. Louis*

Graphite on white wove paper. 16⅝ x 12¾ in. (430 x 323 mm.)

Watermark: Fragment of an unidentified monogram near center of left edge.

Signed at the lower right: *Ingres Del. Rome 1817*

CONDITION:     Ingres reduced the scale of M. Jordan's head, thus heavily abrading the paper around his hair. Formerly affixed to a secondary support, the sheet was thinned from the back, particularly to the left of center and at the lower right, when it was later removed from its old mount. Minor tears along the upper edge and near the center of the right edge have been mended. The drawing has been bleached.

PROVENANCE:     Augustin Jordan (d. 1849); to Baronne Octave Despatys, née Adrienne Jordan (d. 1895); to her son Pierre-Camille-Augustin-Omer Despatys; to his son Pierre-Jérôme Despatys; in 1922 to Wildenstein, Paris, where it was acquired in March, 1923, by Grenville L. Winthrop.

BIBLIOGRAPHY:     Henry Lapauze, "Sur quelques oeuvres inédites de Ingres," *La Renaissance de l'art français*, December, 1922, pp. 649, 652, reprod. p. 650; Zabel, 1930, reprod. p. 378; Mongan, 1944, p. 398, reprod.; Mongan, 1947, no. 12, reprod.; Hans Naef, "Deux dessins d'Ingres, Monseigneur Cortois de Pressigny et le chevalier de Fontenay," *La Revue des Arts*, VII, November-December, 1957, p. 244, fn. 6.

EXHIBITIONS:     Paris, Paul Rosenberg, 1922, *Exposition d'Oeuvres de grands maîtres du dix-neuvième siècle*, no. 49.

Augustin Jordan, the brother of the well-known Restoration orator Camille Jordan, was born at Lyons in 1773. He entered the diplomatic service as a young man, and had his first post under Talleyrand in Vienna. In 1808, he married, in Grasse, Augustine-Louise-Euphrasie de Mauduit Du Plessis (see No. 41). They went to Rome in 1815 where he had been appointed secretary of the French Embassy. The new Ambassador, the first after the fall of the Empire, was Monseigneur Cortois de Pressigny, whose other secretaries were Gabriel de Fontenay and Chevalier Artaud de Montor. The four seem to have been on excellent terms with Ingres. Of the first three, he made portraits which are among his most sympathetic and distinguished. To the fourth, Artaud, he dedicated a drawing of Paolo and Francesca, a subject which he may have known through Artaud's translation of Dante.

Jordan was, like Ingres, in Rome until 1820. He died in Paris in 1849, having outlived his wife and his son. He seems to have possessed an extraordinarily winning character, for the notices of his death speak of his capacity for friendship among all sorts of people and of his remarkable and unfailing kindness. The drawing represents him with his daughter Marie-Alexandrine-Adrienne who, in 1833, became the Baronne Antoine-Nicolas-Octave Despatys. She died in Paris in 1895.

*Fogg Art Museum, Harvard University,*
*Bequest of Grenville L. Winthrop, 1943.840*

Graphite on white wove paper. $17\frac{7}{16}$ x $12\frac{13}{16}$ in. (443 x 326 mm.)

Watermark: Fragment of an unidentified monogram near center of the left edge.

Signed at the lower right: *Ingres Del. Rome 1817*

CONDITION: The drawing was formerly affixed to a secondary support. When it was later removed, the paper suffered a general thinning on the back. A two-inch tear at the upper right and a hole, which has not affected the surface, along the lower right edge have been mended. The drawing which had darkened to brown was bleached.

PROVENANCE: Augustin Jordan (d. 1849); to Baronne Octave Despatys, née Adrienne Jordan (d. 1895); to her son Pierre-Camille-Augustin-Omer Despatys; to his son Pierre-Jérôme Despatys; in 1922 to Wildenstein, Paris, where it was acquired in March, 1923, by Grenville L. Winthrop.

BIBLIOGRAPHY: Henry Lapauze, "Sur quelques oeuvres inédites de Ingres," *La Renaissance de l'art français,* December, 1922, pp. 649, 652, reprod. p. 651; Zabel, 1930, reprod. p. 381; Mongan, 1944, p. 398, reprod.; Mongan, 1947, no. 13, reprod.; Hans Naef, "Deux dessins d'Ingres, Monseigneur Cortois de Pressigny et le chevalier de Fontenay," *La Revue des Arts,* VII, November-December, 1957, p. 244, fn. 6.

EXHIBITIONS: Paris, Paul Rosenberg, 1922, *Exposition d'Oeuvres de grands maîtres du dix-neuvième siècle,* no. 50.

Madame Jordan, née Augustine-Louise-Euphrasie de Mauduit Du Plessis was born in 1789 in Quimperle (Finistère). She married Augustin Jordan in October, 1808, in Grasse. She is represented with her son Gabriel who, according to Lapauze (1922), was born in 1813. This seems a possible error, however, since the child in the drawing is surely less than seven years old. The fact that his name is Gabriel would seem to indicate that he had been named for the Ambassador or for Fontenay (see under No. 40), both of whom were called Gabriel. Madame Jordan died in Paris, 25 August 1847, having survived her son.

*Fogg Art Museum, Harvard University,*
*Bequest of Grenville L. Winthrop, 1943.841*

Graphite on cream-colored wove paper. 8⅝ x 6¹⅜ in. (218 x 173 mm.) Oval inscribed in graphite: 204 x 169 mm.*

Signed at the lower right: *Ingres Delineavit | in roma 1817*

CONDITION:      The drawing has been bleached and extensively mended at the very edges. The paper has been thinned just above the sitter's braids where Ingres erased to change her coiffure.

PROVENANCE:      Acquired in Padua (?) by A. Clinton Landsberg, 1930's.

BIBLIOGRAPHY:      Raymond Charmet, "La Collection Lehman à l'Orangerie," *Arts,* 12 June 1957, reprod. p. 14.

EXHIBITIONS:      Paris, Musée de l'Orangerie, 1957, *La Collection Lehman de New York,* no. 139; Cincinnati, Cincinnati Art Museum, 1959, *The Lehman Collection,* no. 279, reprod.; New York, 1961, no. 23, reprod.

When A. Clinton Landsberg acquired this drawing in Italy in the nineteen-thirties, it was stretched on a rough wooden panel. In the course of the years, this wood backing had stained the paper and placed it under considerable strain. It was judged wise to remove the drawing before it discolored further and before the page cracked.

At that time the enchanting if slightly pouting, pale-eyed young lady was said to be a Principessa Falzacappa. Further researches in Italy revealed that the traditional identification of the sitter had been incorrect, and that the drawing in fact represented a Principessa Fiano of Rome and Padua. We have not been able to add anything more to her history. Mrs. Landsberg has confirmed the name Fiano (September, 1966) but can find no additional information regarding the drawing in the papers of her late husband.

*Robert Lehman, New York*

Jongres Delineant
in roma 1819

Graphite. 9 x 7 in. (230 x 178 mm.)*

Signed at the lower left: *Ingres.* | *Del rome* | *1817.*

PROVENANCE:   Frau Louis Köster, née Marie-Auguste-Friederike Reinhold; Martin Birnbaum, New York, to an anonymous private collector.

BIBLIOGRAPHY:   K. A. Varnhagen von Ense, *Tagebücher,* VII, Zurich, 1865, p. 220, entry for 17 June 1850; Hans Naef, "Zwei unveröffentlichte Ingreszeichnungen," *Schweizer Monatshefte,* March, 1956, pp. 649-54; Hans Naef, "Ein unveröffentlichtes Meisterwerk von Ingres im Staedelschen Kunstinstitut," *Die Weltkunst,* 15 February 1958, p. 9.

Louise-Sophia-Henrietta Ritter was born 24 September 1788 at Niemburg-am-Weser. She was the sister of the Dutch Ambassadress to Rome (No. 34) and doubtless sat to Ingres when she visited her sister in the Eternal City. To date, nothing more is known of her history. The Ritters and the Reinholds seem to have foregathered in Rome between 1815-17, because there also exists an Ingres portrait drawing of the Ambassador's sister, Susanne-Eleanore-Friedericke Reinhold. The latter was acquired by the Staedel Institute, Frankfurt, from the sitter's descendants in 1958.

*Private Collection*

Ingres.
fec. rome
1817.

Graphite on cream-colored wove paper. 11⅝ x 8½ in. (288 x 215 mm.)

Signed at the lower left: *Ingres*

CONDITION:     Minor tears at the sides and along the lower edge have been mended.

PROVENANCE:     Comte Turpin de Crissé (d. 1859) to la Comtesse Turpin de Crissé, née Adèle de Lesparda (d. 1861); to her sister Louise de Lesparda (d. 1875); to her brother Baron Auguste de Lesparda; to his widow la Baronne Lesparda, née Louise-Pauline de Magallon (d. 1903); to her son Baron Paul de Lesparda; Anonymous Sale, Paris, Hôtel Drouot, 20 November 1929, no. 9, reprod.; Jacques Mathey, Paris; Gilbert Lévy, Paris; Matthiesen Gallery, London; César M. de Hauke, Paris, to Walter C. Baker, 1948.

BIBLIOGRAPHY:     Agnes Mongan, *One Hundred Master Drawings,* Cambridge, 1949, p. 136, reprod.; Claus Virch, "The Walter C. Baker Collection of Master Drawings," *The Metropolitan Museum of Art Bulletin,* New York, June, 1960, p. 316; Claus Virch, *Master Drawings in the Collection of Walter C. Baker,* New York, 1962, p. 7, no. 92, reprod.

EXHIBITIONS:     Paris, 1934, no. 13; Paris, Musée des Arts décoratifs, 1934, *Les Artistes français en Italie de Poussin à Renoir,* no. 530; Brussels, Palais des Arts, 1936, *Ingres-Delacroix,* no. 28; London, Matthiesen Gallery, 1938, *A Century of French Drawings,* no. 91; Cambridge, Fogg Art Museum, 1948-49, *Seventy Master Drawings,* no. 56; New York, Metropolitan Museum of Art, 1960, *The Walter C. Baker Collection of Master Drawings,* no. 14; Poughkeepsie, Vassar College, and New York, Wildenstein, 1961, *Vassar College Centennial Loan Exhibition,* no. 81, reprod.

Adèle de Lesparda, Comtesse Turpin de Crissé, was born in 1789. She married Turpin de Crissé 16 November 1813 and survived him by two years, dying in May, 1861. They had no children. We know little about her beyond what her husband said of her, in summing up his own life. "Trois sentiments profonds ont rempli (ma vie): une tendresse pour ma mère, mon amour pour mon art, celui que je suis encore pour ma femme après vingt ans de mariage."

*Walter C. Baker, New York*

Graphite on cream-colored wove paper.  11⅞ x 8⅛ in.  (295 x 227 mm.)

Signed at the lower left: *Ingres.*

CONDITION:      The edges of the paper have suffered tears and minor losses.

PROVENANCE:     Comte Turpin de Crissé (d. 1859) to la Comtesse Turpin de Crissé, née Adèle de Lesparda (d. 1861); to her sister Louise de Lesparda (d. 1875); to her brother Baron Auguste de Lesparda; to his widow la Baronne Lesparda, née Louise-Pauline de Magallon (d. 1903); to her son Baron Paul de Lesparda; Anonymous Sale, Paris, Hôtel Drouot, 20 November 1929, no. 8, reprod.; Jacques Mathey, Paris; Gilbert Lévy, Paris; Matthiesen Gallery, London; César M. de Hauke, Paris, to Walter C. Baker, 1948.

BIBLIOGRAPHY:   E. S., "A Century of French Drawings from Prud'hon to Picasso," *Burlington Magazine,* LXXII, June, 1938, p. 308, reprod. p. 306; René Huyghe and Philippe Jaccottet, *Le dessin français au XIXe siècle,* Lausanne, 1948, p. 173, reprod. p. 12; Agnes Mongan, *One Hundred Master Drawings,* Cambridge, 1949, reprod. p. 134; Claus Virch, "The Walter C. Baker Collection of Master Drawings," *The Metropolitan Museum of Art Bulletin,* n.s., XVIII, June, 1960, p. 314; Claus Virch, *Master Drawings in the Collection of Walter C. Baker,* New York, 1962, p. 7, no. 91, reprod.

EXHIBITIONS:    Paris, 1934, no. 12; Paris, Musée des Arts décoratifs, 1934, *Les Artistes français en Italie de Poussin à Renoir,* no. 530; Brussels, Palais des Arts, 1936, *Ingres-Delacroix,* no. 29; London, Matthiesen Gallery, 1938, *A Century of French Drawings,* no. 90; Cambridge, Fogg Art Museum, 1948-49, *Seventy Master Drawings,* no. 55; Philadelphia, Philadelphia Museum of Art, 1950-51, *Masterpieces of Drawings,* no. 83, reprod.; New York, Metropolitan Museum of Art, 1960, *The Walter C. Baker Collection of Master Drawings,* no. 14; Poughkeepsie, Vassar College, and New York, Wildenstein, 1961, *Vassar College Centennial Loan Exhibition,* no. 81, reprod.

Lancelot-Théodore, Comte Turpin de Crissé, was born in Paris in 1782 and died there in 1859. The son of a marquis who emigrated at the time of the Revolution and died in Philadelphia in 1795, Lancelot-Théodore was left without means. He became an artist, was Chamberlain to Josephine, and from 1821-30, the Inspector General of Fine Arts. An active collector of objets d'art and antiquities, he bequeathed his collection to the museum at Angers. He visited Italy in 1808, 1818 and 1824, sketching various landscapes to illustrate his *Souvenirs du Golfe de Naples,* published in 1828. One of the many landscape pen drawings is now in the Fogg Museum; others are preserved in the Louvre. Baron Taylor, who delivered the elegy at his funeral, justly and exactly estimated their quality: "L'élégance, le regularité doucement austère de sa vie, se réfletaient dans ses ouvrages. Ils exprimaient un talent regulier et pur, un coeur et un esprit tranquille, attachés à des principes invariables."

Although the portrait is not dated, Ingres must have drawn Comte Turpin de Crissé, judging from his costume and apparent age, on his Italian journey of 1818.

*Walter C. Baker, New York*

Graphite on white wove paper. 8 x 6¼ in. (203 x 160 mm.)*

Signed at the lower right: *Ingres | à Cortot. | 1818 | rome.*

PROVENANCE:   Jean-Pierre Cortot (d. 1843) to his niece and sole heir Mlle. Désirée-Marie-Charlotte Eymery, later Comtesse Désiré-François-Brice de Comps (d. 1884); to her daughter Mlle. Marguerite-Cécile-Elisabeth de Comps (d. 1911); M. A. McDonald, New York, to James H. Lockhart, Jr.

BIBLIOGRAPHY:   Galichon, 1861, p. 357; Delaborde, 1870, no. 274; Blanc, 1870, p. 236; Gatteaux, no. 78, reprod.; Jouin, 1888, pp. 36 ff.; Lapauze, 1911, reprod. p. 174; Louis Hourticq, *Ingres,* Paris, 1928, reprod. pl. 50; Robert McDonald, "The Print Collection of James H. Lockhart, Jr.," *Carnegie Magazine,* May, 1939, reprod. p. 39; Alazard, 1950, p. 62.

EXHIBITIONS:   Paris, 1861, no. 48; Paris, 1867, no. 328; Pittsburgh, Carnegie Institute, 1939, *100 Prints and Drawings from the Collection of James H. Lockhart, Jr.,* p. 133, reprod.

Jean-Pierre Cortot was born in Paris in 1787. His parents were humble shopkeepers. The boy had almost no schooling as his later letters, written in a personal phonetic spelling, make clear. With his parents' permission he entered, at the age of thirteen, a modest sculptor's studio where he began to study and work. In 1809, at the age of twenty-two, he won the *grand prix de Rome.*

Ingres must have known him from the moment Cortot arrived at the Villa Medici, for Ingres' own term as a student was not completed until 1810. In 1815 he painted Cortot's portrait, a simple head, turned three-quarters front (Musée des Beaux-Arts, Algiers). In 1818 he drew him as we see him here, elegant, relaxed, nonchalant, a handsome and sensitive rather than powerful person. The painted portrait and the drawing remained in the possession of Cortot's collateral descendants through the first quarter of the twentieth century.

Ingres and Cortot had much in common. Both were from simple backgrounds, both were ambitious, both were tremendous workers. Cortot left Rome in 1819, a year ahead of Ingres, and returned to Paris where he became one of the most prolific and most successful sculptors of the nineteenth century. Today we are familiar with many of his works without knowing that he is their author. Among them are the large bas-relief on the east façade of the Arc de Triomphe, the sculptured pediment of the Chambre des Deputés, and many other reliefs and figures which ornament well-known public buildings in Paris.

*James H. Lockhart, Jr., Geneseo, New York*

 yngres
à Cortot
1811
Rome

Graphite. 4⅝ x 3⅜ in. (119 x 87 mm.)*

Signed at the middle left: *Ing*

PROVENANCE:  Madame Mame, Tours (Sale, Paris, Georges Petit Gallery, 26-29 April 1904, no. 105) to François Flameng (Sale, Paris, Georges Petit Gallery, 26-27 May 1919, no. 123, reprod.); Henry Lapauze; Madame Bialix; Jean Dieterle & Co., Paris, to Tony Mayer, 1950 (Sale, Paris, Charpentier Gallery, 3 December 1957, no. 9, reprod.); André Weil, Paris, to Marianne Feilchenfeldt, 1958; to John S. Newberry, 1958.

BIBLIOGRAPHY:  Philippe de Chennevières, "Exposition rétrospective des portraits," *Gazette des Beaux-Arts,* XII, 1 August 1889, p. 131; Lapauze, 1911, reprod. p. 237; Louis Lacrocq, "Les portraits de Madeleine Ingres, née Chapelle," *Memoires de la société des sciences naturelles et archéologiques de la Creuse,* XXI, 1919-21, p. XXVII and fn. 2; Charles Saunier, "Collection François Flameng," *Les Arts,* no. 167, 1918, p. 22, reprod.; Frederick Cummings, "Romantic Portraitist, Three Drawings by Ingres," *Bulletin of the Detroit Institute of Arts,* XLIV, No. 4, 1965, pp. 73, 77, reprod. p. 74.

EXHIBITIONS:  Paris, 1911, no. 124; Paris, 1921, no. 233; Paris, Guiot Gallery, 1953, *Deux Écritures de Goya à Lautrec,* no. 4; New York, Slatkin Galleries, 1959, *French Master Drawings,* no. 69, reprod.; Cambridge, Fogg Art Museum, 1960, *Thirty-three French Drawings from the Collection of John S. Newberry,* no. 19, reprod., New York, 1961, no. 33, reprod.

Traditionally, this sensitive and beautiful drawing has been called a portrait of Madame Borel. Madame Borel, half sister of Madame Madeleine Ingres (see No. 64), was born in Chalons-sur-Marne in 1775. Her husband followed the same trade as her father. He was a simple carpenter. In spite of tradition, it is difficult to see in this distinguished, refined, sad face, with its enframement of an elaborate and surely fashionable turban, a simple lady from a French provincial town. Looking at the drawing purely from the point of view of the development of Ingres' graphic style, we should like to date it about 1815-18, the moment of the finest English portraits. The kind of turban which she wears, however, rarely appears before 1818.

At the end of Ingres' Roman sojourn, he used a pencil that was not as finely pointed as it had been a decade earlier. Gradually, he developed a softer touch, even using a softer graphite which made a darker and somewhat broader line. If our dating is correct, and the traditional title is also correct, Madame Borel must have made a trip to either Rome or Florence. There is no record of any such journey in the archives or in letters. The signature, although by Ingres, is not the one which he used when signing portraits. It is the one he hastily scribbled on drawings which generally stayed in the studio.

When one considers the scale, the pose and the signature, is it not possible that the drawing is a fragment, all that remains of a figure seated on a Louis XVI chair or loveseat, her right elbow resting on the chair's arm, the line of its back visible behind her left shoulder? Was it once a portrait drawing of Ingres' normal size, or was it a study for a larger drawing now unknown? We are inclined to favor the former of these two possibilities.

*Detroit Institute of Arts,*
*Bequest of John S. Newberry, 1965*

Oil on canvas. 18⅛ x 13¾ in. (460 x 349 mm.)

PROVENANCE: Paul Lemoyne; Jean-François Gigoux (Sale, Paris, 6 May 1861); P. A. Cheramy (Sale, Paris, 5-7 May 1908, lot 212); Henri Haro (Sale, Paris, 12-13 December 1911, no. 217); Henry Lapauze (Sale, Paris, 21 June 1929, no. 54).

BIBLIOGRAPHY: Delaborde, 1870, p. 254, no. 136; Lapauze, 1901, p. 235 (Ingres, Cahier IX) and p. 248 (Ingres, Cahier X); Lapauze, 1911, pp. 163-64, reprod. p. 179; Wildenstein, 1954, no. 130, p. 190, reprod. fig. 82; *Handbook of the William Rockhill Nelson Gallery of Art, Atkins Museum,* Kansas City, 1959, 4th ed., p. 119, reprod.; Hans Naef, "Notes on Ingres Drawings, II," *The Art Quarterly,* XX, Autumn, 1957, pp. 298-301.

EXHIBITIONS: Paris, 1911, no. 24; Copenhagen, Musée Royal, 1914, *Exposition d'Art français du XIX^e siècle,* no. 118; Paris, 1922, *Cent Ans de Peinture Française* (illustrated on catalogue cover); Pittsburgh, Carnegie Institute, 1930, *Old Masters Exhibition,* no. 23; San Francisco, M.J. de Young Memorial Museum in co-operation with the California Palace of the Legion of Honor, 1934, *French Painting, Fifteenth Century to the Present Day,* no. 114; Springfield, etc., 1939-40, no. 24; New York, 1961, no. 26, reprod.

Ingres painted this portrait sketch sometime between 1817, when Lemoyne arrived in Rome, and 1820, when Ingres left for Florence. Lemoyne had come to Rome at his own expense after failing the competition for the *grand prix* in sculpture. He became well established in his adopted city and never returned to France. In 1831 the French Ambassador Chateaubriand commissioned Lemoyne to design a monument to Poussin, still preserved in the Church of San Lorenzo in Lucina. Between 1835 and 1838 he worked on a monument to another Romanized Frenchman, Claude Lorrain. This was placed in San Luigi dei Francesi where it is seen today by visitors who come to study the more highly esteemed Contarelli Chapel by Caravaggio. In 1835, Lemoyne was made a member of the Accademia di San Luca. He died in Rome in 1873, shortly before his ninetieth birthday.

Ingres made a second portrait of Lemoyne, a pencil drawing, in 1841, before he left Rome at the close of his term as Director of the Villa Medici. The drawing is dedicated to "ami Lemoyne" and to the last time the two friends saw each other. It shows an elegant but more reserved Lemoyne, with eyes as penetrating and fiery as those in the youthful portrait (Naef, *op. cit.,* reprod. p. 298).

Ingres must have admired this early oil sketch for when he learned in his old age that Lemoyne had sold it, he was angry. "The wretch has sold himself," he cried. The aged artist insisted that the Besançon artist, Jean Gigoux, who had bought it, never sell it. Gigoux describes the incident (Naef, *op. cit.,* p. 301). Gigoux, who had bought the portrait of Dédéban at the same time as the Lemoyne canvas, promised Ingres never to sell either. He kept only one half of his promise, auctioning the Lemoyne in 1861 and bequeathing the Dédéban to the museum of Besançon.

*William Rockhill Nelson Gallery of Art,*
*Atkins Museum of Fine Arts, Kansas City*

Graphite. 11¼ x 8 in. (285 x 203 mm.)

Signed at the lower left: *Ingres à Madame Taurel | Roma 1819.*

PROVENANCE:  Mme. Taurel (d. 1836) to her husband André-Benoit Barreau Taurel (d. 1859); Taurel family; Federico Madrazo (d. 1894); Comtesse de Béhague (Sale, London, Sotheby's, 29 June 1926, no. 101, reprod.); Knoedler, New York, to John Nicholas Brown, 1927.

REPRODUCTIONS:  Engraved by Charles-Edouard Taurel, 1885.

BIBLIOGRAPHY:  Charles-Edouard Taurel, *L'Album T.*, Amsterdam and the Hague, 1885, pp. 2, 15, reprod. opp. p. 3 (engraving); Lapauze, 1901, p. 268; Lapauze, 1911, reprod. (after the engraving) p. 178; Lapauze, *Briant,* 1911, p. 48; Zabel, 1930, p. 381; H. E. van Gelder, "Ingres en de familie Taurel," *Maandblad voor beeldende Kunsten,* January, 1950, pp. 5, 7, reprod. after the engraving; Alazard, 1950, p. 37; Naef, 1960, p. 27, fn. 52; p. 22; mentioned under No. 24, pl. 16; fig. 7; Hans Naef, "Ingres und die Familien Thévenin und Taurel," *Nederlands Kunsthistorisch Jaarboek,* XVI, 1965, pp. 138-42, 154-55, no. 4.

EXHIBITIONS:  Cambridge, 1929, no. 85; Springfield, etc., 1939-40, no. 28, reprod.; New York, 1961, no. 28, reprod.; Cambridge, Fogg Art Museum, 1962, *Forty Master Drawings from the Collection of John Nicholas Brown,* no. 17.

André-Benoit Barreau Taurel, who was born in Paris in 1794, won the *prix de Rome* for engraving in 1818. In the last months of that year he took up residence as a *pensionnaire* at the Villa Medici. In June, 1819, he married Mlle. Claire Thévenin, the adopted daughter of Charles Thévenin, the French Academy's director, who had succeeded Guillon Lethière in 1817. The young couple received as a wedding present an album filled with drawings by the young French artists then in Rome. Ingres' contribution to the album was a group of seven superb portrait drawings. This portrait of the bridegroom was among them.

Taurel stands in the open air on the Bosco Terrace of the Villa Medici, a view of the dome and towers of Borromini's S. Agnese in Agone at the left (see Naef, 1960, fig. 7, p. 122, and pl. 16 for reproductions of related landscape drawings from the Montauban Collection). It is known that Ingres and his wife were very fond of the bride (see under No. 67). This drawing suggests that the bridegroom also found favor in the artist's sight, for he has given us a very sympathetic, lively and subtle portrait of a not very handsome young man.

Taurel was appointed professor of engraving at the Fine Arts Academy in Amsterdam in 1828. He lived in Amsterdam until his death in 1855. An artist with technical gifts of a high order, he had a great influence on engraving in Holland. His own work was mostly in portraiture, very accomplished but somewhat cold.

*John Nicholas Brown, Providence*

*ingres à Madame Taurel*
*Rome 1819.*

Oil (ochre, umber, white and red) on canvas primed with ochre. 18 x 14½ in. (458 x 370 mm.)

CONDITION:    The canvas is in very good condition. There are only a few spots of inpainting in the ground area and minor repairs in the figure's torso.

PROVENANCE:    Ingres to Paul Delaroche, 1831; to the latter's son Horace Delaroche; Wildenstein to Grenville L. Winthrop, 1940.

BIBLIOGRAPHY:    Delaborde, 1870, pp. 208-09; Wildenstein, 1954, p. 188, no. 126, pl. 17; Schlenoff, 1956, pl. xvi.

Working within an extremely limited range of colors, Ingres has given to both the full-length figure and the fragmentary study an extraordinary sense of life. Presumably a direct study from the model, this oil sketch undoubtedly preceded the small *Perseus and Andromeda* (No. 51). The artist is still experimenting with the position of the head and hands. A drawing related to this figure has been on the London art market (Marlborough Gallery, February-March, 1951, no. 28, reprod.). The legs and hands of the figure are in the pose of this sketch, but the head is turned three-quarters front.

Ingres presented this oil sketch to Paul Delaroche in 1831, the year when Delaroche's painting *Cromwell Opening the Coffin of Charles I,* now almost forgotten, created a sensation at the Salon.

*Fogg Art Museum, Harvard University,*
*Bequest of Grenville L. Winthrop, 1943.248*

Oil on canvas. 7⅛ x 5⅞ in. (182 x 150 mm.)*

Signed at the lower left: *Ingres.*

PROVENANCE: Probably A. Didot (Sale, Paris, 6-8 May 1828, lot 25); Hauguet (Coutan-Hauguet Sale, Paris, 16-17 December 1889, lot 21); Henri Beraldi, Paris; Gallimard, Paris; Cassirer, Berlin; McNeill Reid, Edinburgh.

BIBLIOGRAPHY: Delaborde, 1870, p. 208; L. Vauxcelles, "La Collection Gallimard," *Les Arts,* no. 81, September, 1908, reprod.; Wildenstein, 1954, no. 125, p. 188, fig. 77; Martin Davies, *National Gallery Catalogues, French School,* London, 1957, p. 119, no. 9.

In discussing Ingres' studies for the various versions of *Roger and Angelica,* Delaborde mentions this oil sketch. He comments upon it as a "première pensée de la composition" (*op. cit.*). Indeed, it may be a preliminary idea, but it is not for a Roger and Angelica. It would seem that Ingres first had in mind a Perseus and Andromeda; for the figure who swoops out of the sky to strike at the monster has the magic sword, the winged sandals and the mirror-shield, the attributes of Perseus. The theme may then have shifted, possibly after Ingres had read Ariosto's *Orlando Furioso* (see No. 52). Later Ingres himself was furious with the critic, Kératry, who had found fault with Ingres for the "Gothicism" of his style, when the latter referred to the 1819 *Roger and Angelica* as "Andromeda" (Lapauze, 1911, pp. 194-96). This oil sketch indicates, however, that Ingres did have an Andromeda in mind at one time.

Martin Davies (*op. cit.*) points out that the small *Oedipus* in the National Gallery of London is almost the same size as the *Andromeda* and that both were in the Didot Sale in 1829. He suggests that there may have been some connection between the two classical subjects.

*Private Collection*

Graphite on white wove paper. 6¾ x 7¾ in. (171 x 197 mm.)

Signed at the lower left: *Ingres.*

CONDITION:     There are numerous tiny holes in the paper, made by the compass which Ingres used in
               transferring the design. (The sheet is also very lightly squared with graphite.) The
               drawing, heavily foxed when it entered the Fogg Collection, has been bleached. The
               right and bottom edges are ragged.

PROVENANCE:    Fernand Guille; Edgar Degas (Sale, Paris, Georges Petit Gallery, 26-27 March 1918, no.
               213); Scott and Fowles, New York, to Grenville L. Winthrop, 1924.

BIBLIOGRAPHY:  Delaborde, 1870, no. 32, pp. 207-09; Mongan, 1947, reprod. no. 14; Martin Davies, *Na-
               tional Gallery Catalogue, French School,* London, 1957, p. 119; Daniel Ternois, *Ingres et
               son temps, Montauban, Musée Ingres, Peintures* (Inventaire des collections publiques
               françaises, 11), Paris, 1965, cited under no. 160.

The drawing illustrates an episode from Ariosto's *Orlando Furioso* (Venice, 1570), Canto x,
stanzas xcii ff., which had obviously captured Ingres' imagination with particular force. In Cahier
x, he wrote an extensive description of both the setting and the dramatic action (Delaborde, 1870, p.
208). Roger, riding his hippogriff along the coast of Brittany, sees Angelica chained to a rock, ex-
posed to the attacks of a hideous monster. Had he not seen her tears, the pink of her cheeks and the
breeze moving her hair, he would have thought her of alabaster. He rides toward Angelica, killing
the monster with his lance.

The painted first version of *Roger Delivering Angelica,* now in the Louvre, was shown in the
Salon of 1819. Ingres returned to the subject in the eighteen-thirties (National Gallery, London) and
in 1841 (Montauban), altering the composition somewhat each time. Martin Davis (*op. cit.*) thinks
that of the twenty-two drawings at Montauban which are studies for the painting, two correspond
closely to the Fogg drawing (Momméja, nos. 455 and 456). The position of the monster, the lance
and the size and shape of the rock, all relate the Fogg drawing to the 1819 version.

His own work reveals that Degas, who formerly owned the drawing, studied it carefully.

*Fogg Art Museum, Harvard University,*
*Bequest of Grenville L. Winthrop, 1943.859*

Very soft graphite on cream-colored wove paper. 7⅜ x 5½ in. (183 x 140 mm.)*

Signed and dated in the lower right corner: *Ingres | rome | 1820*

CONDITION:    The drawing was formerly coated with a resinous varnish. This film, which covered all but the light areas along the right edge, has been removed.

PROVENANCE:    Paul Rosenberg, Paris, ca. 1921; Mme. de Cassigneul (Sale, Paris, Hôtel Drouot, 28-29 March 1925, no. 25, reprod.).

BIBLIOGRAPHY:    Galichon, 1861, p. 47; Delaborde, 1870, no. 423; Blanc, 1870, p. 240; Lapauze, 1921, reprod. p. 240; Louise Burroughs, "Drawings by Ingres," *The Metropolitan Museum of Art Bulletin,* IV, February, 1946, reprod. p. 160.

EXHIBITIONS:    Paris, 1861; Paris, 1867, no. 394; Paris, 1921, no. 92.

Ursin-Jules Vatinelle was a sculptor, medallist and gem engraver. Born in Paris 23 July 1798, he won the *grand prix de Rome* in 1819. Ingres therefore drew this portrait of the student in Vatinelle's first year at the Villa Medici, just before Ingres' departure for Florence. Vatinelle never married, and when he died in Paris, 16 September 1881, he left no relatives. Today his work is little known. *The Biographical Dictionary of Medallists* (London, 1916, Volume VI) mentions some of his medals.

*The Metropolitan Museum of Art,*
*Bequest of Grace Rainey Rogers, 1943*

Graphite (in the body) and charcoal (in the drapery) over stylus lines on heavy white wove paper (the verso of a frontispiece, *Plans de maisons romaines tirée* (sic) *du plan antique de Rome, conservé au Capitole*, engraved by Cipriani). 15⅜ x 7⅝ in. (390 x 194 mm.)

Signed in brown ink at the lower right: *Ingres*

CONDITION:     Brown stains have been produced by the acid ink in which the engraving was printed. The drawing has been abraded along the upper left side. At the lower right a tear, 1¾ inches in length, has been mended.

PROVENANCE:     Marquis de Biron; Grenville L. Winthrop, 1934.

BIBLIOGRAPHY:     Mongan, 1944, pp. 404-05; Daniel Ternois, *Ingres et son temps*, Montauban, Musée Ingres, *Peintures* (Inventaire des collections publiques françaises, 11), Paris, 1965, chronology discussed under no. 164.

In 1819, the Minister of the Interior commissioned Ingres to paint an altarpiece for the Cathedral of Montauban, commemorating the "Vow of Louis XIII," a vow which placed the Kingdom of France under the protection of the Virgin. Ingres was dissatisfied with the subject. He would have preferred to paint an Assumption of the Virgin. It is on the Feast of the Assumption, 15 August, that the vow of Louis XIII is commemorated in France. The government authorities were adamant in their choice, but the discussions concerning the subject delayed the project's start until 1821.

Ingres, in Florence at the time, made numerous studies for the composition such as this one for the Madonna's robes. It is clearly under the influence of Raphael. Delaborde records a statement by Ingres which indicates that the reflections of Raphael were intentional: "All that I will tell you is that I spare nothing in order to make the thing Raphaelesque and mine."

Ingres finished the painting in 1824 and exhibited it with great success in the Salon of that year. It was the first painting by Ingres to receive both a critical and a popular success, marking a turning of the tide which had been, until then, against him. The painting was placed in the Cathedral in 1826 where it can be seen today on an altar in the left aisle.

A close examination of the Fogg drawing reveals that the nude figure beneath the drapery was drawn with a sharply pointed instrument. This suggests that the artist traced the essential outline of a nude which he had previously drawn and then drew the drapery in charcoal, and the head and neck in graphite. Related drawings for the figure of the Madonna are in the collections of the museums at Dijon and Montauban. The Montauban drawing is also distinguished by Ingres' use of a stylus to outline the figure.

*Fogg Art Museum, Harvard University,*
*Gift of Grenville L. Winthrop, 1942.67*

Ingres Del
Flor 1813.

Soft graphite on very thin white wove paper, heightened with white chalk. 17¹⅛ x 13¾ in. (450 x 349 mm.)

Signed at the lower left: *Ingres Del.* | *Flor 1823.*

CONDITION:     Exposure to light has slightly discolored the paper. When it was removed from a former mount, the edges were damaged; numerous small holes and tears, particularly at the lower left, have been mended. A large tear near the hem of the skirt at the left was patched with an adherent which subsequently stained the paper. The sheet of paper was originally imperfect, marred by a long horizontal fault above the hemline. This weakness has been somewhat aggravated by later treatment.

PROVENANCE:     Albert Goupil; bequest of Charles Jalabert in 1898 to Jean-Léon Gérome (d. 1904); Mme. Jean-Léon Gérome (d. 1911); Mme. Aimé Morot, née Gérome, to Grenville L. Winthrop, 1932.

BIBLIOGRAPHY:     Delaborde, 1870, no. 247; Blanc, 1870, p. 240; Émile Molinier, "La collection Albert Goupil," *Gazette des Beaux-Arts,* XXXI, 1 May 1885, p. 388; Lapauze, 1903, no. 97, reprod.; Louis Gonse, *Les chefs-d'oeuvre des Musées de France, sculpture, dessins, objets d'art,* Paris, 1904, p. 93; Miller, 1938, pp. 13, 14; Mongan, 1944, pp. 398 f., reprod.; Mongan, 1947, no. 16, reprod.; Jean Cassou, *Ingres,* Brussels, 1947, pl. 36; Martin Birnbaum, *The Last Romantic,* New York, 1960, p. 189.

EXHIBITIONS:     Paris, 1867, no. 540; Paris, École des Beaux-Arts, 1884, *Dessins de l'école moderne,* no. 393; Paris, 1911, no. 118.

Like the portrait of her husband (No. 56), the portrait of the Countess Antoine Apponyi, née Contessa Teresa Nogarola of Verona, is one of the most beautiful as well as one of the largest of Ingres' drawings. Together they rank among the highest artistic achievements of the artist's Florentine stay. He has placed her, as he placed Count Apponyi, against a Florentine background. At the left is the tower of the Badia, at the right, the Palazzo della Signoria.

If we are correct in our identification, the sitter was both beloved and admired. In Rome she was described, according to Daudet (E. Daudet, *Journal du Comte Rodolphe Apponyi,* Paris, 1913, p. x) as eclipsing the other diplomatic ladies by the richness and elegance of her dress, by her dazzling beauty and "by that heavenly expression which distinguishes her from all the other ladies." In Paris, for a quarter of a century she presided over "le plus beau palais de Paris," the Hôtel d'Eckmühl on the rue St. Dominique, where she received the elite of French society, to whom she was known as "la divine Thérèse." In addition to the portrait miniature mentioned under No. 56, there is another portrait of her reproduced as the frontispiece of Volume II of the *Journal.*

The drawing was precisely copied in April, 1935, by Jean-Alexandre Coraboeuf.

*Fogg Art Museum, Harvard University,*
*Bequest of Grenville L. Winthrop, 1943.848*

Soft graphite with white chalk on very thin cream-colored wove paper. 17⅞ x 13⅝ in. (453 x 346 mm.)

Watermark: JW 1818 (Whatman paper).

Signed at the lower left along the bank of the Arno: *Ingres d. florence 1823.*

CONDITION:    The paper is slightly discolored as a result of exposure to light. The edges, particularly the lower one, were stained by the adherent used in a former mount.

PROVENANCE:    Albert Goupil; Baron Joseph Vitta; Scott and Fowles to Grenville L. Winthrop, 1925.

BIBLIOGRAPHY:    Blanc, 1870, p. 240; Mongan, 1944, p. 398, reprod.; Mongan, 1947, no. 17, reprod.; Jean Cassou, *Ingres,* Brussels, 1947, pl. 37; P. Labrouche, *Les dessins de Ingres,* Paris, 1950, pl. 6.

EXHIBITIONS:    Paris, 1867, no. 584; Paris, 1911, no. 120; Paris, 1921, no. 222.

This drawing and the preceding one first became known when they were lent by Albert Goupil to the Ingres Retrospective Exhibition in 1867. Even at that early date, the identities of the sitters were not given; perhaps they were already lost. Curiously, in the supplement to the catalogue the portraits were listed under widely separated numbers, the lady under no. 540 and the man under no. 584, a circumstance which leads one to presume that at this time they were not considered pendants. However, similarities in scale, size, date, setting and pose seem to indicate that they were created as a pair.

Molinier (see under No. 55), writing in 1885 about the Goupil Collection, mentions only the lady. Neither of the drawings was in the Goupil Sale, 23-27 April 1888, three years later. Separated for some decades, they were again united in the Winthrop Collection only by chance. The man entered the collection in 1925. Seven years later, in 1932, the lady rejoined her cavalier.

Recent research now allows us to associate this dashing portrait with the name of Count Antoine Apponyi, a distinguished Austrian diplomat. Two documents tend to confirm this identification. The first is a painting, *Portrait of a Man,* signed and dated "Jules Ziegler, 1822," now in the collection of Marvin Sadik, Brunswick, Maine. The sitter is undoubtedly the gentleman represented in the Winthrop drawing. Ziegler, a pupil of Heim and Ingres, is not known to have been in Italy in 1822, but a trip of this kind is not improbable. Anne K. Brown, after studying the sitter's costume in the Ziegler portrait, concluded that he was an Hungarian Magnate.

Count Antoine Apponyi (1782-1852) was, in fact, a scion of an ancient and powerful, noble Hungarian family, and the husband of a beautiful Italian, Contessa Teresa Nogarola of Verona. Serving as the Austrian Minister in Florence from 1814 until 1819, Count Apponyi was then promoted to the post of Ambassador in Rome. In 1826, he was appointed Ambassador to Paris where he stayed until 1848.

Secondly, a journal of the Paris years kept by his nephew and secretary, Count Rodolphe Apponyi, and published by Ernest Daudet in 1913, offers further evidence in support of this identification (*Journal du Comte Rodolphe Apponyi, Vingt-cinq Ans à Paris (1826-50),* Paris, 1913). The frontispiece of Volume I reproduces two miniatures, the portraits of Count and Countess Antoine Apponyi. These correspond directly to the so-called "Florentine Cavalier" and the "Lady with the Parasol." As Apponyi had been the Austrian Minister to Florence until 1819, it is very likely that he and his wife returned for a visit in 1823. Ingres, who had painted the portrait of the Russian Minister to Florence, Count Guriev (The Hermitage, Leningrad), in 1821, was not unknown in these diplomatic circles.

*Fogg Art Museum, Harvard University,*
*Bequest of Grenville L. Winthrop, 1943.847*

Soft graphite, heightened with white chalk on dark tan wove paper which has been affixed to a wood-pulp mount. The figure was outlined first with a stylus. Sight measurements: 12¼ x 10⅝ in. (310 x 270 mm.)

Signed in graphite at the lower right: *Ingres*. An inscription above the signature, apparently written by the artist has been erased: *Iliad*. Red stamp of the E.-F. Haro Collection at the lower right (L. 1241).

CONDITION:    As a result of light and the wood-pulp mount, the paper has darkened. The lower left corner has been patched.

PROVENANCE:    É.-F. Haro; T. Edward Hanley, Bradford, Pennsylvania; E. V. Thaw, New York, to Walter C. Baker, 1966.

EXHIBITIONS:    New York, Wildenstein, and Cambridge, Fogg Art Museum, 1961-62, *Paintings and Drawings from the Hanley Collection*, no. 79.

The drawing is a study for the figure representing the *Iliad*, seated on the steps below and at the left of the enthroned Homer. She is balanced by the *Odyssey* who sits at his right on the same step.

There are numerous studies for both figures, posed nude, draped and sometimes with their respective emblems, the sheathed Roman sword of the *Iliad* and the *Odyssey's* oar. A drawing of this figure, nude, is now in the collection of the École des Beaux-Arts, Paris (Giraudon, 14367). An oil sketch in exactly this pose, but with the sword reversed, is in a private collection in Paris (Wildenstein, no. 175).

The antique sources upon which Ingres drew were varied. Personifications of the *Iliad* and the *Odyssey* were known as early as the Hellenistic period, although no statues have survived intact (David Mitten, Harvard University). Ingres therefore turned to reproductions of antique vases for his specific models (see A. Mongan, "Ingres and the Antique," *Journal of the Warburg and Courtauld Institutes,* x, 1947). The drapery style of the *Iliad* was obviously inspired by antique sculpture.

*The Apotheosis of Homer* was commissioned in 1826 as a ceiling decoration for Room IX of the Musée Charles X (Salle Clarac) at the Louvre. It was begun in 1826 and completed just a year later, in time for the Salon of 1827. Removed for the Exposition Universelle of 1855 and sent to the Luxembourg, it was later returned to the Louvre in 1874. A copy by the brothers Balze is in the Salle Clarac, the room for which Ingres painted the picture. Homer sits enthroned, surrounded by his spiritual descendants, ancient and modern. (For Ingres' sources, see Schlenoff, 1956, pp. 148-200.) In 1865, Ingres returned to the subject and executed the large drawing now in the Louvre (Guiffrey and Marcel, 5015), increasing the number of descendants from forty-six to eighty-two.

Wildenstein lists thirty-two oil studies for the painting (nos. 169-200). Momméja describes two hundred drawings related to it, the majority relating to the study of Homer.

*Walter C. Baker, New York*

Graphite and black chalk, heightened with white chalk, on pale brown wove paper. 15½ x 10¾ in.
(393 x 273 mm.)

Watermark: an illegible fragment at the upper right.

Signed in graphite at the lower left: *Ing*

CONDITION:    The drawing has suffered severely from heavy and recurrent foxing. Various methods
              have been used to minimize these disfiguring spots.

PROVENANCE:   Charles A. Loeser.

BIBLIOGRAPHY: Mongan-Sachs, 1940, no. 703, fig. 374.

The drawing is a drapery study for the figure of Virgil. One of a series of bold and beautiful drawings in black and white chalk on brown paper, it proclaims an obvious debt to Ingres' divinity,
Raphael. The brown paper contributed to the forceful effects which Ingres sought, but unfortunately it was of poor quality. When backed with wood-pulp paper or cardboard, such paper often,
as here, developed spots which mar the surface and which cannot be permanently removed.

In the painting a youthful Virgil, clad in white classical drapery, stands to the far left, just beyond
Raphael who is presented to Homer by Apelles. Virgil holds his left hand on his heart. His right,
which does not show in the drawing, shelters Dante whom Virgil presents to Homer.

*Fogg Art Museum, Harvard University,*
*Bequest of Charles A. Loeser, 1932.179*

## 59

STUDY FOR THE DRAPERY OF MOLIÈRE IN THE "APOTHEOSIS OF HOMER"                                                        ca. 1827

Black chalk with stumping on heavy cream-colored laid paper. 12 x 9⅞ in. (305 x 250 mm.)

Signed in graphite at the lower right: *Ingres* | *a Madame* (*Mademoiselle* has been corrected by the artist) | *Sarrazin de Belmont*

Notations in black crayon by the artist: by the hand, *velours;* bottom center, *clair;* behind and below the shoulder, *verte;* at the lower right, *grand clair.*

CONDITION:      The drawing is lightly foxed, especially along the left side.

PROVENANCE:     Marquis de Biron (Sale, Paris, Georges Petit Gallery, 9-11 June 1914, no. 36).

BIBLIOGRAPHY:   M. Benisovich, "The French Drawings of the Metropolitan Museum," *The Burlington Magazine,* LXXXII-III, 1943, pl. IIB, p. 73.

EXHIBITIONS:    Rotterdam, Paris, New York, 1958-59, no. 131, reprod. pl. 92.

The drawing is a study for the cloak of Molière who offers a comic mask to Homer. He stands below and to the right of the *Odyssey,* beneath the outstretched arm of Phidias, with the profile of Racine just behind him, and Boileau between him and the spectator.

The dedication, changed by the artist himself from *mademoiselle* to *madame* is to Louise-Joséphine Sarazin (or Sarrazin) de Belmont (1790-1871), a pupil of Valenciennes, who exhibited at the Salon from 1812 to 1817. Five of her paintings, all Roman landscapes, are preserved in the Musée Ingres, Montauban, three the gift of Ingres, one from Gatteaux and one from the artist herself.

In 1958-59 when the drawing was shown in Rotterdam and Paris, the lender did not share the view that the drawing was related to the figure of Molière. However, two drawings at Montauban (photographs, Resseguie, Montauban) both squared for transfer, one of the figure nude and the other draped, lead us to conclude that the Metropolitan drawing is indeed a study for this figure.

*The Metropolitan Museum of Art,*
*Rogers Fund, 1937*

## 60

STUDIES FOR THE "MARTYRDOM OF ST. SYMPHORIEN": A CROUCHING ca. 1826-34
NUDE YOUTH REACHING FOR A STONE; SEPARATE STUDY OF AN
ARM

Graphite and black crayon on white wove paper with touches of red crayon in the separate arm, squared for transfer. 15⅜ x 19⅝ in. (390 x 498 mm.)

Signed at the lower left (covered by the mat): *Ing.* Inscribed on the verso in brown ink: *Dessins à coller* (crossed out) | *Sous l'orme;* and in graphite: *Cavalier port(e)* | *le Casque* | *tireur* | *porte enseigne.*

CONDITION: Although the drawing has been bleached, foxing is still visible in the left third of the sheet. A hole ⅝ inch high in the biceps of the separate arm, has been inlaid, and numerous old vertical creases have been flattened. A rectangle has been stained by a former wood-pulp mat. The inscription written on the verso in brown ink has also stained the drawing at the upper left.

PROVENANCE: François Flameng (Sale, Paris, Georges Petit Gallery, 26-27 March 1919, no. 124); Maurice Le Garrec to Paul J. Sachs.

BIBLIOGRAPHY: Mongan-Sachs, 1940, no. 702, fig. 373; Alazard, 1950, pl. LXV.

EXHIBITIONS: Hartford, Wadsworth Athenaeum, 1946, *The Nude in Art,* no. 31; Detroit, Detroit Institute of Arts, 1951, *French Drawings of Five Centuries,* no. 27; Rotterdam, Paris, New York, 1958-59, no. 132, pl. 110; New York, 1961, no. 35, reprod.; Cambridge, Fogg Art Museum, and New York, Museum of Modern Art, 1965-67, *Memorial Exhibition, Works of Art from the Collection of Paul J. Sachs,* no. 44, reprod.

A study for the *Martyrdom of St. Symphorien,* the drawing represents a youth who is virtually lost in the final painting, obscured by the crowd behind the saint at the right. The painting was commissioned in December, 1824, at the request of the Bishop of Autun who wished a replacement for the altarpiece by Fra Bartolommeo which had been taken to Paris during the Revolution. It was the bishop who selected the subject, choosing the story of an early local martyr. Ingres had hoped to have the finished work ready for the Salon of 1827. It was not completed, however, until 1834, and then its reception was more than cool. Affronted, the artist wished to leave Paris. He asked for and was given the Directorship of the French Academy in Rome.

There are at least eleven oil sketches for the painting. Two are in the Fogg Museum, but are not in the present exhibition because their condition is problematical. In one of the two, the crouching nude can be seen more clearly than in the finished painting (Wildenstein, no. 214). There are two hundred preparatory drawings at Montauban, and others scattered in various museums. Among the latter is another study of the same youth in the Musée Bonnat, Bayonne.

The Société Eduenne published, in 1856, a twenty-four page *mémoire* giving the history of the painting.

*Fogg Art Museum, Harvard University,*
*Bequest of Meta and Paul J. Sachs, 1965.296*

**61**    THREE MEN ON HORSEBACK, A STUDY FOR THE "MARTYRDOM OF ST.    ca. 1827-34
SYMPHORIEN"

Black chalk on paper. 21⅜ x 16¼ in. (544 x 413 mm.)

PROVENANCE:    Madrazo; Comtesse de Béhague.

BIBLIOGRAPHY:    Mongan, 1947, no. 18, reprod.; Shoolman-Slatkin, 1950, p. 116, pl. 65; Alazard, 1950, pl. LXVI.

EXHIBITIONS:    Springfield, etc., 1939-40, no. 41, reprod.; Hartford, Wadsworth Athenaeum, 1946, *The Nude in Art,* p. 11, no. 32; New York, 1961, no. 42, reprod.

This powerful and thoughtful drawing must have been among the early studies for the *Martyrdom of St. Symphorien.* The dominant figure, carrying the staff and gazing down from his commanding position astride the horse, was transformed in the final composition. The figure at the right, looking up towards the left, took his place behind the Roman centurion who is lightly sketched at the lower right. The squaring of this pointing figure was probably in anticipation of an oil sketch at Montauban which repeats exactly this detail (Wildenstein, no. 217). The centurion, still nude, is again the central figure of a second oil sketch in the Fogg Museum (Wildenstein, no. 213).

Probably the artist worked on the painting too long and too hard, for the finished work has none of the impact, freedom and majestic poise of these figures, and no echo of the brilliant light which plays on them.

*William Rockhill Nelson Gallery of Art,*
*Atkins Museum of Fine Arts, Kansas City*

STUDIES OF LEGS, HANDS AND THE PROFILE OF A HEAD FOR THE
"MARTYRDOM OF ST. SYMPHORIEN"

Graphite. 18 x 12 in. (458 x 305 mm.)

Signed at the lower right: *Ingres;* inscribed in the artist's hand at the upper right: *pour le ... | clair de-miteinte rouge | chaud fort clair pas | autant les angles | blanc;* inscribed near the center beside the palm of a hand: *clair.*

PROVENANCE:    Charles E. Slatkin Galleries to Stephen R. Currier.

BIBLIOGRAPHY:    Jacques Mathey, *Ingres,* Paris, 1945, [pl. 10].

The striding legs are those of the lictor who stands to the left of St. Symphorien. In the painting, he grasps the top of his fasces, holding their points against the ground. In an oil sketch at Montauban, his right arm is bent, his hand against his hip (Wildenstein, no. 215). The legs at the upper left are for a figure behind that lictor; the leg at the right edge, for the lictor to the right of the saint. The profile is that of a bearded man just behind him. The hand grasping the baton is a study for one of the mounted soldiers seen behind the saint, between his upraised arms.

The many changes made between these vigorous sketches and the finished painting suggest that Ingres was still experimenting with the details of the composition, inventing his forms with extraordinary freshness and vitality. Powerful studies such as this and the one of the *Horsemen* (No. 61) not only speak for the thoroughness of Ingres' working methods, but also demonstrate his dedication to the project, thus helping to explain his acute disappointment when the finished work won only faint praise, even from his friends.

*Stephen R. Currier, New York*

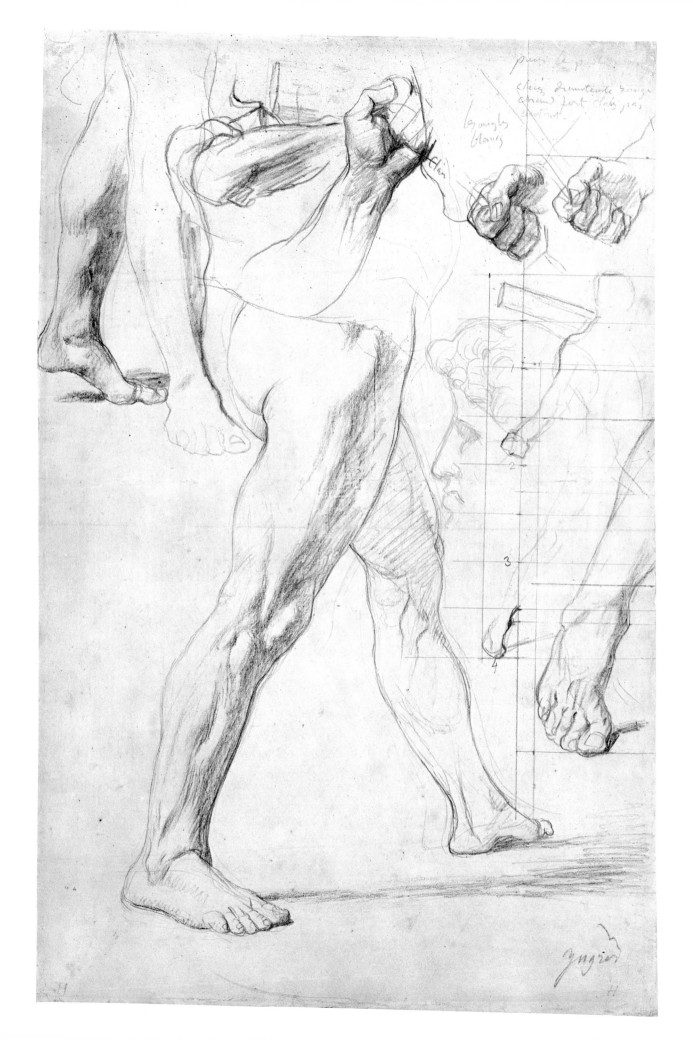

Watercolor (violet, magenta, scarlet, yellow, blue, gray, black) over graphite on white laid paper, squared for transfer in red chalk. 10¼ x 7¾ in. (260 x 197 mm.)

Signed in graphite at the lower left: *Ingres.*

CONDITION:      The drawing has presumably been cut from a larger sheet. Damages include small holes, such as those in the curtain at the upper left and along the base of the column at the right, and the large repaired area at the upper right. Revisions in the design by Ingres himself, specifically changes in the scale and position of the throne, are visible.

PROVENANCE:    M. P. Rosenberg.

BIBLIOGRAPHY:  Ternois, 1959, above no. 22.

EXHIBITIONS:   St. Petersburg, 1911, *Exposition centennale de l'art français,* no. 182; New York, Wildenstein, 1963, *Master Drawings from the Art Institute of Chicago,* no. 78.

Charles X (1757-1836) was the fourth child of the dauphin Louis, the son of Louis XV. Before his accession to the throne, as the successor of his brother Louis XVIII, he was known as the Comte d'Artois. He was crowned at Rheims, in 1825, in an elaborate ceremony which sought to restore the solemn ritual of the *ancien régime* and to obliterate the memory of Napoleon's *Sacre* in Notre Dame in 1804. A reactionary royalist who misunderstood both the tempo of his times and the mood of his people, Charles found it expedient to abdicate in 1830. After the so-called July Revolution he was succeeded by his cousin Louis Philippe. Charles withdrew to exile in Britain. He died in Göritz, where he had gone for his health, in 1836.

Ingres was present at the Coronation at Rheims, as David had been in Notre Dame, but we have no "carnet" of the ceremony. He was commissioned to make three drawings to be engraved in an elaborate publication which was to commemorate the occasion, one of Charles X in his coronation robes, one of the Cardinal Archbishop of Rheims, Monseigneur de Latil and a frontispiece representing the alliance of Religion and Royalty. The drawings were made, according to Mommeja, in 1828. The finished drawings of the King and the Cardinal in pen and wash with an elaborate enframement are in the Louvre (nos. 5054 and 5055). A badly damaged watercolor, on tracing paper, the *Alliance of Religion and Royalty,* is in the Fogg Museum (1948.19).

This watercolor seems more closely related to a painting of Charles X in which the figure is one-half life-size than to the Louvre drawing. M. de Fresne ordered the painting, which is now in the Bonnat Museum, Bayonne (Wildenstein, pl. 67). Ingres signed and dated it 1829. At Montauban there are drawings in which Ingres searches out the pose of the figure in studies of the nude; there is a portrait head of the king without the crown and a study of the right arm and ermine tippet.

Here the king wears the crown with the great Regent Diamond made by Frédéric Bapst for his brother. He carries in his left hand the Hand of Justice, which French kings carried from the time of Hugh Capet; in his right, the scepter capped with the figure of Charlemagne, the scepter which had been made into a staff by Louis XIV. In the space for the hand, both scepter and Hand of Justice have been covered with royal velvet embroidered with fleur-de-lis, a change since the opening years of the century when Ingres, as a young man, represented Napoleon carrying them. Only the tips of the banners at Charles' feet show. In the painting the columns and curtains at either side are abandoned and the throne made more prominent.

*The Art Institute of Chicago*

Graphite. 8 x 6 in. (203 x 152 mm.)*

Signed at the lower right: *Madame Ingres | à Sa bonne amie | Madame Thomeguex | Ingres.*

PROVENANCE:    Mme. Pyrame Thomeguex, née Jeanne Gonin; Baron Vitta; R. Langton Douglas; Joseph T. Ryerson.

BIBLIOGRAPHY:    Hans Naef, "Ingres als Portraitist seiner westschweizerischen Freunde," *Du*, xv, August, 1955, p. 18.

EXHIBITIONS:    Paris, 1911, no. 122; Nice, Palais des Arts, 1931, *Ingres*, no. 16; San Francisco, 1947, no. 13.

Madeleine Chapelle was born at Chalons-sur-Marne, in 1782. Her father, a carpenter, married twice. She was the daughter of the second wife, née Jeanne Nicaise. Madeleine went to live with her married sister, Madame Pierre-Antoine Dubreuil, at Guéret, where she supported herself as a modiste. Among the many Imperial functionaries whom Ingres met in the early years of the century in Rome and who were almost his only patrons between 1810-15, was one François-Joseph-Stanislas Mainony de Lauréal, Chief Registrar of the Imperial Court in Rome. De Lauréal was married to Anne-Nicole-Adelaide Nicaise. According to tradition, Ingres was greatly taken with Adelaide's charms. Adelaide, who seems to have been happily married, thought of a cousin who ressembled her to an extraordinary degree, Madeleine Chapelle at Guéret. She made the suggestion of a match to Ingres who proved receptive to the idea, and to Madeleine who greeted the proposal with enthusiasm. Letters passed between Rome and Guéret. The pair seemed amazingly suited to one another, so Madeleine left her home and went to Rome to meet her future husband. The meeting was happy; the marriage took place in San Martino ai Monti, Rome, 4 December 1813. Guillon Lethière (see Nos. 19 and 30) was one of the witnesses. Madeleine proved the perfect wife for the man of genius. They had thirty-six years together before her death in 1849.

When this drawing was first shown, the sitter was said to be Madame Gonin (Ingres Exhibition, 1911). The confusion arose, undoubtedly, because the drawing is dedicated to Madame Thomeguex, née Jeanne Gonin (her portrait is in the Taft Museum, Cincinnati). It appeared for the first time with a correct identification in the San Francisco Exhibition of 1947.

The inscription, in the handwriting of Ingres, but in the name of his wife, is to Jeanne Gonin, sister of Monsieur Gonin (see No. 80) who in 1822 married Pyrame Thomeguex at Fiesole. The Gonins and the Thomegeux were among Ingres' closest friends during his Florentine years (1820-24). There is a presumed portrait of Jeanne Gonin Thomeguex, dated 1825 (Museum of Art and History, Geneva). Given that date, the Geneva drawing must have been made in Paris. It is tempting to believe that Madame Thomeguex accompanied Madame Ingres from Florence to Paris early in 1825, after Ingres' triumph with the *Voeu de Louis XIII,* and that the Kirkland drawing of Madame Ingres was done at that time as a gift to a very good friend. The age of the sitter seems to correspond to her age in 1825, when she was forty-three.

Costume experts doubt that the drawing could have been made before 1830 because of the "mutton chop" sleeves of her dress; but Madeleine Ingres wore full sleeves as early as 1819, as the Alaux painting of Madeleine and her husband in their Roman apartment (Montauban) demonstrates. There Madame Ingres wears a dress with sleeves which are like those in the dress she wears here.

We know that Madeleine was accomplished with the needle. When she lived in Florence, she was in no position to follow fashion; but once back in Paris, the Ingres' financial as well as artistic position was greatly changed. One naturally wonders if the ruffled bonnet is one of her own "confections." In any case, the drawing is one of the most sympathetic, beautiful and serene of the many portraits which Ingres drew of his wife.

*Mrs. Hugh Kirkland, Santa Barbara*

*Madame Ingres à sa bonne amie Madame Chenavaux. Ingres*

Graphite on cream-colored wove paper (Whatman type). Design area: 9⅝ x 7½ in. (245 x 191 mm.)*
See Technical Appendix.

Signed at the lower right: *Ingres à PaPa | et à maman. | 1830.*

CONDITION:    The drawing has been removed from its original cardboard support. Bathing in water
has minimized the discoloration caused by this mount.

PROVENANCE:   The sitter's family until ca. 1934, when it was presumably sold by her niece Mme. Jacquin
de Margerie, née Charlotte-Louise-Marie Rohault de Fleury; Jacques Seligman, New
York, to Miss Edith Wetmore, 1934.

BIBLIOGRAPHY: Delaborde, 1870, no. 368 (unless this is a reference to the other version); Blanc, 1870, p.
238 (unless this is a reference to the other version); Lapauze, 1903, no. 67, reprod.;
Lapauze, 1911, p. 286 (unless this is a reference to the other version); Ulrich Christoffel,
*Klassizismus in Frankreich um 1800,* Munich, 1940, reprod. p. 139; Hans Naef, "Ingres
Portraits of the Marcotte Family," *Art Bulletin,* XL, December, 1958, p. 342, fn. 27, re-
prod. fig. 16.

EXHIBITIONS:  Paris, 1867, no. 379 (label on back).

Marie Marcotte was one of the two daughters of Ingres' very good friend Marcotte d'Argenteuil
(Naef, *op. cit.,* fig. 13). In 1828, Marcotte had married Louise-Marie-Phillipine Becquet, his niece.
A portrait of Phillipine, in the year of their marriage (Naef, *op. cit.,* fig. 14) shows her as a charming person; and the drawings of her children, dedicated to her by Ingres, make plain his deep at-
tachment to the parents as well as the children. He drew this portrait twice. On the version still in
the family, he wrote, *"Oh, que j'aime grand'maman!,"* and at the bottom, *"Ingres à PaPa | et à
Maman | 1830."* On the reverse of this drawing's mount, the baby's father wrote, *"Ma fille Marie à
l'âge de 15 mois. mariée à Alexandre Legentil, mois d'octobre 1846."*

Her marriage took place only two months after Ingres had drawn Marie's portrait again (Naef
*op. cit.,* fig. 19). As happened so often in marriages in the Marcotte family, her husband was also a
relative, a rich, cultivated, scholarly, retiring gentleman of devout and reflective nature. In 1870,
fleeing from Paris to Poitiers, he conceived of the idea of a church at the top of Montmartre, dedicated to the Sacre Coeur. His zeal, shared by his wife, brought the dream to fruition in the build-
ing we all know.

*Yale University Art Gallery,*
*Bequest of Edith Malvina K. Wetmore, 1966*

Ingres à Papa
et à maman.

1830.

Graphite. 12⅝ x 9½ in. (322 x 241 mm.)

Signed at the lower right: *Ingres à Son ami et | confrere Monsieur | Raoul Rochette | 1830.*

PROVENANCE:    The sitter's husband, Desiré Raoul-Rochette (d. 1854); the sitter, Mme. Raoul-Rochette (d. 1878); her grandson, Raoul Perrin (d. 1910); his widow, Mme. Raoul Perrin (d. 1912); their son, Edmond Perrin (d. 1919); Wildenstein, Paris, to Cleveland Museum of Art, 1928.

BIBLIOGRAPHY:    Delaborde, 1870, p. 310, no. 398; Blanc, 1870, p. 239; Lapauze, 1911, p. 286, reprod. p. 281; Henry S. Francis, "A Portrait Drawing by Ingres," *Bulletin of the Cleveland Museum of Art,* xv, February, 1928, pp. 27-29, reprod. p. 21; Louis Hourticq, *Ingres,* Paris, 1928, p. 121, pl. 72; Zabel, 1930, p. 381, reprod. p. 374; Alazard, 1950, p. 84, fn. 31, pl. LXI; Hans Naef, "Ingres und die Familie Raoul-Rochette," *Schweizer Monatshefte,* Supplement, December, 1963, pp. 33-34, reprod. on the cover; Hans Naef, "Ingres et la Famille Raoul-Rochette," *Bulletin du Musée Ingres,* no. 14, December, 1963, p. 17.

EXHIBITIONS:    Paris, 1867, no. 573; Paris, 1911, no. 138; San Francisco, 1947, no. 12, reprod.; New York, 1961, no. 39, reprod.

Madame Raoul-Rochette, née Antoinette-Claude Houdon, was the youngest daughter of the famous sculptor Houdon. She was born in Paris in 1790. Her father modeled a marvelous likeness of her when she was about a year old (Metropolitan Museum of Art), and she is represented at the age of thirteen in Boilly's *The Atelier of Houdon* (Musée des Arts Decoratifs). In 1810, she married Desiré Raoul-Rochette, a noted archaeologist, who later became a close friend of Ingres. In the thirties, he succeeded Quatremère de Quincy as *Secrétaire perpétuel de l'Académie des Beaux-Arts.* Ingres drew a portrait of her husband, now in the Albertina, Vienna, at approximately the same time that he portrayed Mme. Raoul-Rochette.

Claudine, as she was called in the family, enjoyed a very happy married life. Her husband's biographer speaks of "Mademoiselle Claudine Houdon, dont la beauté, la vertu, le mérite répandre sur toute l'existence de Raoul-Rochette d'abord tant de bonheur, puis tant de consolations. De cette union, que le plus leger nuage ne devait jamais troubler, sont nées deux filles, aujourd'hui mariées, l'aînée à Monsieur Perreu's officier-superieure d'artillerie, la plus jeune à l'éminent graveur Calamatta." These two daughters were portrayed by Ingres (see No. 70, Mme. Calamatta). Madame Raoul-Rochette lived to be eighty-eight years old.

*The Cleveland Museum of Art,*
*Purchase from the J. H. Wade Fund*

Ingres à son ami et
confrère Monsieur
Raoul Rochette
1830

Graphite. 7½ x 5½ in. (190 x 140 mm.)*

Signed at the lower left: *Ingres Del | à Ses bons amis Taurel.*

Dated at the lower left: *1830.*

PROVENANCE: André-Benoit Barreau Taurel (d. 1859) and his wife, née Claire Thévenin (d. 1836), to whom the drawing is dedicated; Hippolyte Déstailleur (Sale, Paris, Hôtel Drouot, 19-23 May 1896, no. 797 bis); Comtesse de Béhague (Sale, London, Sotheby's, 29 June 1926, no. 99, reprod.); to Colnaghi, London; Knoedler and Co., New York; to George F. Baker, 1928.

REPRODUCTIONS: Photogravure by Charreyre, 1896.

BIBLIOGRAPHY: Delaborde, 1870, no. 336; Gatteaux, pl. 11; Charles-Edouard Taurel, *L'Album*, I, Amsterdam and The Hague, 1885, p. 15; George Duplessis, *Les portraits dessinés par J.-A.-D. Ingres*, Paris, 1896, no. 16, reprod.; Lapauze, 1901, p. 266 (reference to the photogravure by Charreyre); Boyer d'Agen, *Ingres d'après une correspondance inédite*, Paris, 1909, reprod. pl. 14; Lapauze, 1911, reprod. p. 279; Louis Lacrocq, "Les portraits de Madeleine Ingres, née Chapelle," *Memoires de la société des sciences naturelles et archéologiques de la Creuse*, Guéret, 1919-21, XXI, p. 25; Raymond Bouyer, "Les grandes expositions, L'exposition d'art hollandais et l'exposition Ingres," *Revue de l'art ancien et moderne*, Paris, June, 1921, reprod. p. 54; E. H. van Gelder, "Ingres ende Familie Taurel," *Maanblad voor beeldende Kunsten*, Amsterdam, January, 1950, p. 5, pl. 4; Hans Naef, "Ingres und die Familien Thévenin und Taurel," *Nederlands Kunsthistorisch Jaarboek*, XVI, 1965, pp. 119-57, no. 8, p. 157, reprod. p. 147.

EXHIBITIONS: New York, 1961, no. 38, reprod.

In 1819 when the Taurels were married in Rome, Ingres drew a portrait of the bridegroom on the terrace of the Villa Medici as a wedding gift for the young couple (No. 49). Three years before, he had drawn the future Mme. Taurel and her dog. The Taurels, to whom this double portrait of the artist and his wife is dedicated, remained good friends of the artist after they all returned to France from Rome. In 1828, Taurel was appointed professor of engraving at the Amsterdam Academy of Fine Arts, a post he continued to occupy until the close of his life. We would like to suggest that once again Ingres made a present to his friends.

The date at the lower left is in harder graphite than the inscription. The inscription in fact covers an earlier inscription which has been erased. Both are in the artist's own hand. The figure of Mme. Ingres dominates the page and is the focus of the design to such a degree that the self-portrait of the artist seems an afterthought. It is in a slightly grayer graphite, and the handling is less incisive than in the brilliant drawing of Mme. Ingres. Were it not for the date, we would have considered the drawing a farewell gift to the Taurels when they moved to Amsterdam. Whether they returned to Paris for a visit in 1830 and the artist then made the drawing, or whether he then added his own likeness to a drawing he had made two years before, must remain a speculation. Calamatta, who was constantly in touch with Ingres and who had first gone from Rome to Paris at Taurel's request, may have acted as emissary.

*Mrs. George F. Baker, Locust Valley, New York*

Ingres Del.
à ses bons amis flandrin

Soft graphite on tracing paper which has been affixed to laid paper. 6⅞ x 8⅛ in. (176 x 206 mm.)

Inscribed at the lower left: *Main de M. Bertin.*

Signed in the lower center: *Ing.*

Red stamp of the E. F. Haro Collection at the lower left (L. 1241).

CONDITION:   Fragments of the tracing paper were lost either at the time the drawing was executed, as in the contour of the thumb, or later as the sheet deteriorated. One loss of this kind at the upper left, ⅜ in. in length, has been crudely patched.

PROVENANCE:  Etienne-François Haro; Thibaudeau; Henri Lehman (Sale, Paris, Hôtel Drouot, 2-3 March 1883, no. 201); Comtesse de Béhague; her daughter, Comtesse de Béarn; acquired by Grenville L. Winthrop in 1931.

BIBLIOGRAPHY:  Galichon, 1861, p. 356; Lapauze, 1911, pp. 290-98, reprod. p. 284; Mongan, 1944, pp. 402-03, reprod. p. 404; *Art News,* XLV, March, 1946, reprod. p. 26; Agnes Mongan, *One Hundred Master Drawings,* Cambridge, 1949, p. 138, reprod.; Ternois, 1959, cited above, no. 14.

EXHIBITION:  Paris, 1861.

Louis-François Bertin (1766-1841), generally regarded as the father of modern French journalism, founded and directed the famous *Journal des Débats,* a paper which continued to flourish after his death under the direction of his younger brother and then under that of his two sons. Because of his opposition to Napoleon in the early years of the century, he was first officially silenced and then exiled. He returned to Paris, however, after Napoleon's downfall. From 1823 until the revolution of 1830, his paper was the recognized organ of the constitutional opposition, but in 1830 he gave his support to the July Monarchy.

Ingres claimed to be completely a-political, but obviously he found the personality of the great bourgeois figure sympathetic. Ingres' pupil Amaury-Duval (*L'atelier d'Ingres,* Paris, 1875, pp. 193-95) recounts the difficulties Ingres encountered in finding the expressive pose. Numerous studies have been preserved, including one in the Musée Ingres and another in the Metropolitan Museum which show M. Bertin standing. Another study for the same hand as the Fogg drawing, now in the collection of the École des Beaux-Arts, was exhibited in Paris in 1949. The finished portrait (Louvre) is dated 1832.

*Fogg Art Museum, Harvard University,*
*Bequest of Grenville L. Winthrop, 1943.853*

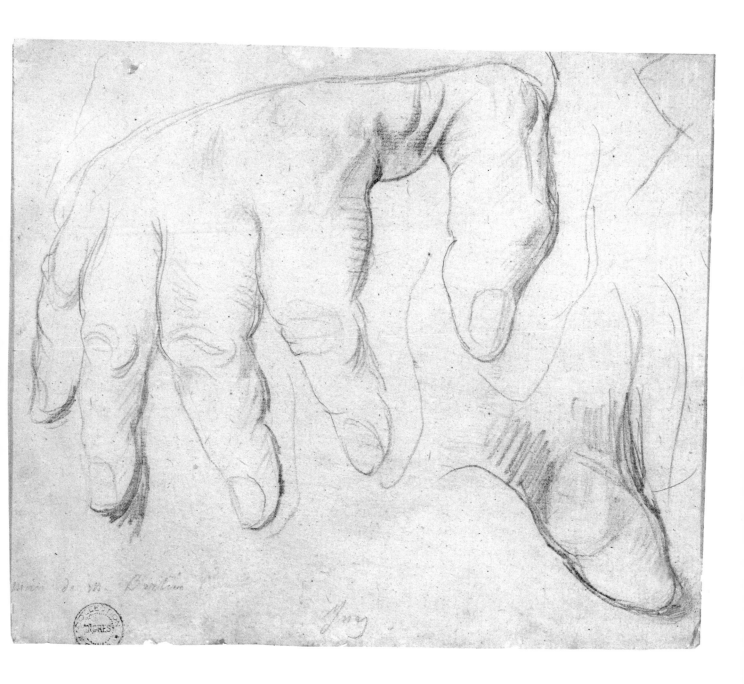

Graphite on cream-colored wove paper. 9 9/16 x 7 7/16 in. (242 x 188 mm.)

Signed at the lower right: *Ingres. | 1833.*

PROVENANCE: The sitter, Marquis Guy-Marie-Emmanuel Legentil de Paroy (d. 1840); his widow, Marquise Legentil de Paroy, née Philippine-Sophie-Fréteau de Pény; their son Marquis Guy-Mériadec Legentil de Paroy (d. 1871); his daughter, Comtesse Jacques de Douglas, née Yvonne Legentil de Paroy (d. 1905); her husband Comte Jacques de Douglas (d. 1924); their son, Comte Jean de Douglas (d. 1929); Sale, Paris, Hôtel Drouot, 7 December 1929 (without catalogue); Albert Meyer, Paris; Jean A. Seligman Gallery, Paris; Robert Treat Paine II, Brookline (d. 1943); his son, Richard C. Paine (d. 1965).

BIBLIOGRAPHY: Delaborde, 1870, no. 389; Lapauze, 1911, p. 286; Seymour de Ricci, *Dessins du dix-huitième siècle: Collection Albert Meyer*, Paris, 1935, no. 42 (as "Lord Douglas").

EXHIBITIONS: Paris, 1934, no. 30 (as "M. de Douglas"); New York, Jacques Seligman Gallery and Cambridge, Fogg Art Museum, 1934, *One Hundred Years of French Art, 1800-1900, Watercolors and Drawings by Fifty French Artists*, no. 8 (as "Lord Douglas"); Boston, Museum of Fine Arts, 1939, *Art in New England, Paintings, Drawings, Prints from Private Collections in New England*, no. 183 (as "Archibald, Second Baron Douglas"); Springfield and New York, 1939-40, no. 43 (as "Archibald, Second Baron Douglas").

This drawing was not exhibited until 1929, when it appeared in an auction at the Hôtel Drouot, Paris, after the death of Comte Jean de Douglas. The sitter was then believed to be a member of the great Douglas family, and the portrait was thus labeled "*Monsieur de Douglas*." A year later it was called "*Lord Douglas*" and ten years later, "*Archibald, second Baron Douglas*." In fact, the sitter is the great-grandfather of the above-mentioned Comte Jean de Douglas. He was Guy-Marie-Emmanuel Legentil, Marquis de Paroy, artist and writer, whose touching memoirs were published by Etienne Charavet in 1895.

The Marquis de Paroy, born in Paris, 10 July 1784, became an officer (chef d'escadre). He and his wife, Philippine Fréteau de Pény, whom he married in 1817, belonged to the intricately interrelated Cabanis, Condorcet, Grouchy and Mercier-Dupaty families who gave to France distinguished figures in art, literature, the law, medicine and the army. He was a distant cousin of the sculptor Dupaty whose likeness was drawn by Ingres in Rome in 1810.

The Marquis de Paroy died in Paris, 13 March 1840. Conclusive proof of the identification will be published by Dr. Naef in a forthcoming article.

*Mrs. Richard C. Paine, Boston*

Ingres
1833.

Graphite. Sight measurements: 9¼ x 7 in. (235 x 177 mm.)*

Inscribed at the upper left: *M^lle Josephine Raoul Rochette.* Signed at the lower left: *Ingres del | 1834*

PROVENANCE:    The sitter's parents M. and Mme. Desiré Raoul-Rochette; Raoul Perrin (d. 1910); his widow Mme. Raoul Perrin (d. 1912); their son Edmond Perrin (d. 1919); Kraushaar Galleries, New York; H. V. Allison & Co., New York, to Chauncey Stillman, 1946.

BIBLIOGRAPHY:   Delaborde, 1870, no. 400; Blanc, 1870, p. 239; Lapauze, 1911, p. 286, reprod. p. 311; Louis Hourticq, *Ingres,* Paris, 1928, pl. 76; Ella Siple, "Art in America," *Burlington Magazine,* LXXV, December, 1939, p. 249; Hans Naef, "Ingres und die Familie Raoul-Rochette," *Schweizer Monatshefte,* Supplement, December, 1963, pp. 10-11, reprod. on the back cover.

EXHIBITIONS:    Paris, 1867, no. 575; Paris, 1911, no. 144; Springfield, etc., 1939-40, no. 49.

Joséphine, the younger daughter of Monsieur and Mme. Raoul-Rochette (see No. 66), was born in March, 1817, in Paris. In 1840, she became the wife of Luigi Calamatta, a close friend of Ingres who engraved many of his compositions. A painter, Joséphine began to exhibit at the Salons after her marriage. She received considerable critical acclaim (see Baudelaire, *Salons of 1845 and 1846*). Her marriage, on the other hand, was not a happy one. The Restoration Raoul-Rochettes and Calamatta, a patriotic follower of Garibaldi, could have had little in common. When her husband, then a professor at the Brera, Milan, died in 1869, she immediately entered a convent.

The Calamatta's daughter Lina, their only child, married George Sand's son, Maurice Dudevant (see No. 4). Josephine's talent was warmly praised by Lina's *belle-mère* (see *l'Artiste,* II, 1885, p. 89).

*Chauncey Stillman, New York*

Mlle Josephine Raoul Rochette.

Ingres del
1834

Graphite on white wove paper.  12⅝ x 9½ in.  (320 x 240 mm.)

Signed at the lower right: *Ingres a | Mademoiselle | he^tte Lorimier | 1834*

PROVENANCE:    Mlle. Henriette Lorimier (d. 1854); Henry Lapauze Collection (Sale, Paris, Hôtel Drouot, 21 June 1929, no. 16, reprod. p. 9); Jacques Mathey; Charles P. Curtis, Boston; J. K. Tannhauser Gallery, New York, to David Daniels.

BIBLIOGRAPHY:   Hans Naef, "Vier Ingres-Zeichnungen," *Pantheon,* XVIII, no. 1, 1960, pp. 35-43, p. 42 reprod.; Mongan, 1962, no. 720, reprod.

EXHIBITIONS:    Boston, Museum of Fine Arts, 1939, *Art in New England,* no. 184; Springfield, etc., 1939-40, no. 30; Montreal, Montreal Museum, 1953, *Five Centuries of Drawing,* no. 185, reprod.; New York, Charles E. Slatkin Galleries, 1959, *French Master Drawings, XVI-XX Centuries,* no. 67, reprod.; Minneapolis, Minneapolis Institute of Art, 1960, *Drawings, Paintings and Sculpture from Three Private Collections,* no. 28; New York, 1961, no. 45, reprod.

François-Charles-Hughues-Laurent Pouqueville was born 4 November 1770 at Merlerault (Orne). His is among the most colorful careers of Ingres' sitters. As his tombstone in Montparnasse tells us, he was an Honorary Member of the Academy of Medicine, a Consul General of France in Greece, a member of the Académie des Inscriptions et Belles Lettres, a Chevalier of the Legion of Honor and l'Ordre du Sauveur. In addition he served with the Napoleonic forces in Egypt, then was, in turn, a prisoner of the Barbary pirates and the Turks. He lived as a prisoner for years in Greece. Profiting from his loneliness, he studied the geography of the country and its diseases, learning modern Greek while not neglecting ancient Greek art and literature. His medical publications were also noteworthy. He died in Paris, 20 December 1838, never having been married. He named as his sole heir, Henriette-Elizabeth-Marthe Lorimier, who erected the monument at the Montparnasse cemetery to his memory and to whom this drawing is dedicated. Her portrait by Ingres is in the Pushkin Museum, Moscow. It bears an inscription to Pouqueville.

*David Daniels, New York City*

Ingres à
Mademoiselle
M<sup>elle</sup> Lorimier
1834

Graphite on white wove paper. 12⅝ x 9⅜ in. (322 x 239 mm.)

Signed at the lower left: *Ingres*. Underneath is the shadow of a previous inscription which has been erased and is now illegible. Although the signature is in Ingres' own hand, the date has been written by a later hand: *1834*. The date is undoubtedly correct, for the same numerals are still visible in the erased inscription.

Black stamp of the Léon Bonnat Collection at the lower right (L. 1714).

PROVENANCE:    Léon Bonnat; Edgar Degas (Sale, Paris, Georges Petit Gallery, 26-27 March 1918, no. 205, reprod.); Mme. de Lassigneul (Sale, Paris, Hôtel Drouot, 28-29 May 1925, no. 27, reprod.); Jacques Seligmann, Paris; César de Hauke to Thomas N. Metcalfe, 1926; his widow, Elizabeth Paine Metcalfe.

BIBLIOGRAPHY:    Zabel, 1930, p. 382.

EXHIBITIONS:    Cambridge, 1929, no. 84, p. 31, pl. ii.

The drawing was made in the year that saw the completion of the *Martyrdom of St. Symphorien* and the *Portrait of Count Molé,* the beginning of *Stratonice,* and the execution of a remarkable group of portrait drawings. Unfortunately the sitter has been nameless for at least a generation. Even when examined under ultra-violet light, the erased dedication has not yielded a clue to her identity. Enough remains, however, to make it clear that the inscription was in Ingres' handwriting.

The artist did not respond with his usual warmth to the personality of his gracious subject. On the other hand, he was obviously delighted with the complex ripples and folds of her elaborate costume.

*Elizabeth Paine Card, Boston*

Graphite on white wove paper. 9½ x 7⅜ in. (242 x 186 mm.) *

Signed along the lower edge: *Ingres à Ses bien bon amis Monsieur et | Madame Gonin. 1834*

CONDITION:      The drawing has suffered random abrasions, particularly in the area of the sitter's left temple. The losses have been minimized by retouching in white chalk. (See Technical Appendix for further discussion.)

PROVENANCE:    Jean-Pierre Gonin and his wife Louise, née Lafon; Eugène Féral (Sale, Paris, Hôtel Drouot, 22-24 April 1901, no. 211); H. N. Calman, London, to Mrs. Charles W. Phinney, née Marian Harris, ca. 1951.

BIBLIOGRAPHY:  Lapauze, 1911, p. 213; Agnes Mongan, "Three Drawings by Ingres," *The Art Quarterly,* XVIII, no. 2, 1955, pp. 180 ff., reprod.; Hans Naef, "Ingres als Portraitist seiner west-schweizerischen Freunde," *Du,* XV, August, 1955, p. 18, reprod.; Hans Naef and Louise Burroughs, "Ingres et les familles Gonin, Thomegeux et Guerber," *Genava,* n.s., XIV, Fall, 1966, no. 14, reprod.

EXHIBITIONS:   New York, 1961, no. 43, reprod.

In 1820, shortly after his arrival in Florence from Rome, Ingres and his wife made the acquaintance of the Gonins (see Nos. 80 and 81). Like so many of his friendships it was lifelong. The Florentine years were difficult ones for the artist; he was very poor and struggling to produce a great work of art. The warmth, friendliness, simplicity and affection of the kindly Swiss family meant a great deal to him. Later, with the betterment of his fortune and the increase of his fame, his regard for them did not decrease. It was with great pleasure that, in December, 1834, on his way to Rome to take up his duties as the newly appointed Director of the French Academy, Ingres and his wife stopped briefly in Florence and had an opportunity to see their old friends whom they had not seen for ten years. The Gonins welcomed Ingres warmly.

It was during that brief visit that Ingres made this drawing of one of the Gonins' sons and dedicated it to the parents. The artist did not write the sitter's name. The Gonins had four sons, one of whom died young. The others were Étienne born in 1813, Constantin born in 1818, and Antoine born in 1819. The young man in the drawing has been identified as Étienne by Mrs. Bryson Burroughs, née Louise Guerber, a descendent of the Gonin-Guerber family. The possibility cannot be totally excluded, however, that it might be one of the younger brothers. Young men matured early a century ago, and the sensitive, handsome, slightly hesitant youth of the drawing could be fifteen or sixteen years old.

All three young Gonins were, like their father, in business. Étienne came to the United States. After a few years he suffered a stroke, so he returned to Berne where he died, in 1864, at the home of his sister Jeanne-Rose-Henrietta Gonin Guerber.

*Fogg Art Museum, Harvard University,
Gift of Marian Harris Phinney, 1952.73*

Ingres à ses bien bons amis Monsieur et
Madame Gouin. 1834

Graphite heightened with white chalk on tracing paper which has been affixed to laid paper. 7$\frac{1}{16}$ x 8½ in. (178 x 215 mm.)  The rectangle is irregular.

Inscribed at the upper left: *main de M le C$^{te}$ Molè* (over an earlier inscription that had been erased).

Signed at the lower right: *Ing.*

Red stamp of the E. F. Haro Collection at the lower right (L. 1241).

CONDITION:    This is the upper half of the sheet on which the studies for both the right and left hands were drawn. The paper is discolored as a result of exposure to light, and lightly foxed. The white heightening is somewhat effaced.

Graphite heightened with white chalk on tracing paper which has been affixed to laid paper. 7$\frac{5}{16}$ x 8$\frac{7}{16}$ in. (186 x 214 mm.)  The rectangle is irregular.

Inscribed at the upper left: *main de M. Molè.*  Inscribed at the lower right: *i$^d$ de C$^{te}$ Molè.*

Signed at the lower right: *Ing.*

Red stamp of the E. F. Haro Collection at the lower right (L. 1241).

CONDITION:    The same as the left hand, with one exception. The tiny spots are caused by imperfections in the paper, not by mold.

The following references apply to both drawings.

PROVENANCE:    Étienne-François Haro; Thibaudeau; Henri Lehmann (Sale, Hôtel Drouot, 2-3 March 1883, no. 201); Comtesse de Béhague to her daughter, Comtesse de Béarn; acquired by Grenville L. Winthrop in 1931.

BIBLIOGRAPHY:  Galichon, 1861, p. 356; Lapauze, 1911, pp. 320-21, reprod. p. 312 and p. 315; Mongan, 1944, pp. 402-03; Ternois, 1959, above no. 129; Mongan, 1962, nos. 721 and 722, reprod.

EXHIBITIONS:   Paris, 1861; Paris, 1867, no. 234.

Louis-Matthieu Molé (1781-1855) was by inheritance and conviction an aristocrat and a monarchist. Undoubtedly influenced by his early experiences—his father returned to Paris from exile too soon and lost his head on the scaffold in 1794—young Molé, the scion of a family who had figured for centuries in French history, made his way coolly and without passion, serving capably if not brilliantly whatever government came to power. He won Napoleon's approval through his publication *Essais de Morale et de Politique* (1808). He was Minister of Foreign Affairs in the first cabinet of Louis Philippe, but served only three months. From 1837-39 he was President of the Cabinet. In 1839 he retired to the Chamber of Peers where his role seemed modeled on that of the Liberal English peers. He posed for Ingres in 1834. In these rapid studies of Molé's hands, Ingres has captured the refined character of the sitter, a man disengaged almost to the point of indifference, it seemed to some of his contemporaries, yet carrying out his duties well.

The drawings throw unexpected light on Ingres' method of working. The two hands were once on a single sheet, for the slight curve of the lower border in the page for the left hand corresponds precisely to the upper edge of the study for the right hand. It is clear that as he revised the portrait's design (see Ternois, 1959, nos. 129-31), Ingres chose to reverse their position. He cut the page, then placed the right hand, holding the magnifying glass with an elegant gesture, above the relaxed left arm, resting nonchalantly on the back of the chair.

*Fogg Art Museum, Harvard University,*
*Bequest of Grenville L. Winthrop, 1943.850-851*

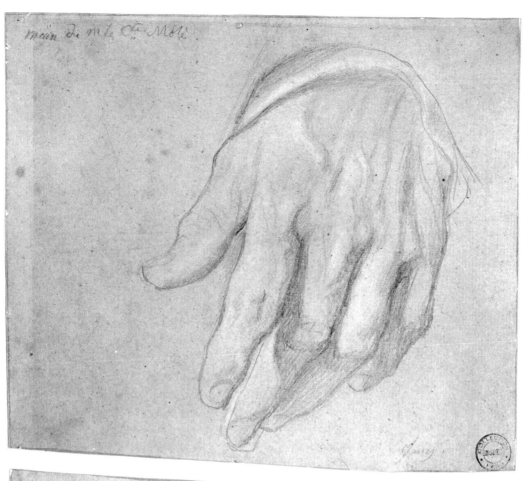

Main de m.l. C.e Molé.

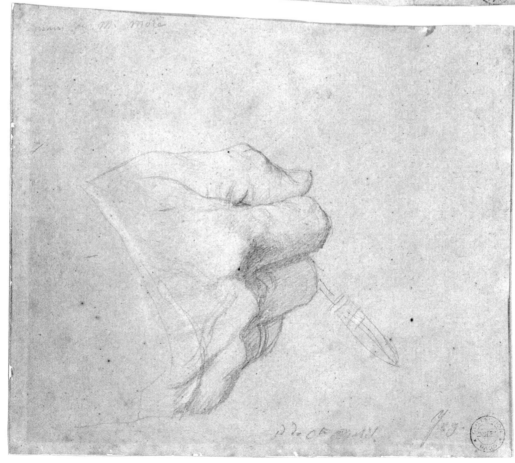

main de m.e Molé.

Graphite. 12¾ x 9¾ in. (324 x 248 mm.)

Signed at the lower left: *à Madame | horace Vernet, | Ingres Del | 1835 | a Rome.*

PROVENANCE: The sitter's mother, Mme. Horace Vernet, née Louise Pujol; the sitter's husband, Paul Delaroche (d. 1856); Delaroche-Vernet family, Paris, until 1952; Jean Dieterle and Cie., Paris; Knoedler, New York, to Mrs. C. Suydam Cutting, née Helen McMahon (Sale, New York, Savoy Art and Auction Galleries, 25-26 June 1964, no. 102).

BIBLIOGRAPHY: Delaborde, 1870, no. 424; Stuart Preston, "Ingres," *House and Garden,* CIV, October, 1953, reprod. p. 169 (incorrectly identified as Mme. Horace Vernet); Hans Naef, "Notes on Ingres Drawings, Part II," *Art Quarterly,* XX, Autumn, 1957, pp. 289-91, fig. 1 (as "Mlle. Louise Vernet"); Mark Roskill, "Ingres: Master of the Modern Crisis," *Art News,* LX, April, 1961, pp. 27 ff., p. 58, reprod. p. 27 (as "Mme. Vernet").

EXHIBITIONS: Newark, Newark Museum, 1954, *From the Collection of Mrs. Suydam Cutting,* no. 1, reprod. (as "Mme. Vernet"); New York, 1961, no. 47, reprod. p. 27.

Louise Vernet was the daughter of the painter Horace Vernet and the great-granddaughter of Moreau le Jeune. Horace, who seems to be the only man Ingres called by his first name (for he so refers to him in his letters), preceded Ingres as director of the French Academy in Rome (1829-34). Amaury Duval, Ingres' pupil, has left a description of the gaiety and worldiness of the Academy under Vernet's regime, when the nobilities of Rome, the people of fashion, the diplomatic corps and the high functionaries of the church all mingled at the Vernet's brilliant social occasions. Louise, with her gentle manner and lovely presence, was an ornament to the company.

On 25 January 1835, just before the Vernet's departure from Rome, Louise married the painter Paul Delaroche, then thirty-seven years of age. Delaroche had traveled to Italy with Henri Delaborde to study Italian religious painting before undertaking a commission to paint the cupola of the Madeleine. While in Rome, Delaroche painted an angel's head, Louise serving as his model. Louise Delaroche lived only ten years after her marriage, but they were ten years of great happiness. She and her husband were hosts to a group of talented and distinguished guests who frequented their home in the rue de la Tour des Dames. Two sons and her husband survived her.

Ingres must have made this sensitive and expressive portrait of her just after his arrival to take over from her father as the Academy's director.

*Ian Woodner, New York*

à Madame
horen Vernet,

Jngres Del
1835
à Rome

Graphite. 10¼ x 14⅜ in. (261 x 367 mm.)

PROVENANCE:    Émile Wauters, Paris (Sale, Amsterdam, Frederik Muller, 15-16 June 1926, Lugt supplement, no. 911); Mathias Komor to a private collector, New York, 1965.

BIBLIOGRAPHY:    Frederic Lees, *The Art of the Great Masters,* Boston, 1913, p. 168, fig. 188.

EXHIBITIONS:    Newark, Newark Museum, 1961, *Nineteenth-Century Master Drawings,* no. 2, reprod.

As Schlenoff has demonstrated (*op. cit.,* pp. 237 ff.), Ingres had a lifelong preoccupation with the theme of the *Illness of Antiochus* or, as it is more commonly called, *Stratonice.* As a student of David, he was undoubtedly familiar with his master's representation of that theme, a canvas which remained in David's atelier. He would also have known a painting of the same subject by Girodet (1793 or 1795) and the opera by Méhul, one of his favorite composers. Ingres probably saw a production of the latter which Napoleon attended, 20 January 1806. The Emperor was so moved that he had it played again the same evening. Ingres owned the musical score of the opera and took it with him to Rome.

In Rome, as early as 1807, he planned a small painting of the subject, mentioned in a letter to M. Forestier. He even completed a careful drawing (Louvre, 5022) for which his friend the architect Bury (see No. 8) made the background. If the painting from that study was ever finished, it has long since disappeared from sight. Nor do we know the whereabouts of a version painted in 1825. The latter, although not located and not illustrated, is described as a first idea for the Chantilly painting (Wildenstein, no. 125). If that is so, it cannot be connected with the early Louvre drawing. There Antiochus is at the left, Stratonice at the right, in a design that is nearer in the conception of form and contour to Flaxman than are the later versions.

In 1834, the Duc d'Orléans commissioned Ingres to paint for him a Stratonice to be a pendant to Delaborde's *Death of the Duc de Guise.* Ingres finally finished the picture in Rome in 1840, after years of struggle.

This study for Antiochus seems to us one of the first ideas for the Chantilly painting. Although Antiochus is at the right, rather than the left as he is in the 1807 drawing, the position of his arms and his head is closer, in its suggestive rather than explicit movements, to that early version than it is to the contorted movements finally chosen for the Antiochus in the Chantilly painting (1840), or to the variants of 1860 and 1866.

*Private Collection, New York City*

Oil on canvas. 18⅝ x 25 in. (474 x 635 mm.)

PROVENANCE: J.-A.-D. Ingres (Sale, 27 April 1867, lot 6); Mme. Ingres; Louis Bazille, Montpellier; Pierre Leenhardt (Sale, Paris, Georges Petit Gallery, 4 May 1922, no. 29); Alphonse Kann; stolen by the German and recovered after World War II; Jacques Seligmann to Cleveland Museum of Art, 1966.

BIBLIOGRAPHY: Delaborde, 1870, p. 220, no. 45; Léopold Mabilleau, "Les dessins d'Ingres au musée de Montauban," *Gazette des Beaux-Arts,* XII, 1894, pp. 177-201; H. Lemonier, "A propos de la Stratonice d'Ingres," *La Revue de l'Art,* XXXV, 1914, pp. 81-90; Lapauze, 1911, pp. 350, 353-60; Wildenstein, 1954, p. 210, no. 224, reprod. p. 226, fig. 181; Schlenoff, 1956, pp. 239-45; Wolfgang Stechow, *"The Love of Antiochus with Faire Stratonica," Bulletin du Musée National de Varsovie,* v, 1964, p. 11, no. 1 (Addenda to *"The Love of Antiochus with Faire Stratonica in Art," Art Bulletin,* XXVII, 1945, pp. 221-37).

EXHIBITIONS: Cleveland, The Cleveland Museum of Art, 1966, *Golden Anniversary Acquisitions,* pp. 232, 280, no. 62, reprod. p. 233.

The story of Antiochus and Stratonice, based on a true story of the time of Alexander the Great, has had a long literary, musical and pictorial history (see Stechow, *op. cit.*). Antiochus, son of Seleucus, ruler of Syria, lies mortally ill of a mysterious illness. His father, overcome with despair, kneels at the foot of his son's bed, his sorrowing head down, his arms outstretched. At the far side of the bed the physician, Erasistratus, stands with his hand over the heart of Antiochus. Stratonice has entered the room and the doctor, feeling Antiochus' heart suddenly leap, divines the cause of the young man's illness. He is in love with his father's young wife. When Seleucus was told the cause of his son's illness, legend says he gave up Stratonice who then married Antiochus.

When the Duc d'Orléans gave Ingres the commission for the painting in 1834, the artist was determined to paint a picture of outstanding quality. As usual, however, he had struggles and qualms that endured until after the finished painting was sent from Rome to Paris (see correspondence with Gatteaux, quoted by Delaborde, *op. cit.,* pp. 215-20). According to the catalogue of the Ingres Sale in 1867, this painting, which was never finished, was begun in 1834. It would then pre-date the Chantilly painting. Indeed there are many changes that lead one to conclude that it is an oil sketch study. It is definitely smaller in scale (18⅝ x 25 in. against 22½ x 38⅝ in.). The proportions are different; here the design is not as emphatically horizontal. There is no baldachin over the bed, no shield, and no dramatic curtain. The short column on the raised platform seems without any particular meaning, there is no statue of Alexander, and the floor has a different pattern. The subject of the wall painting in the background, *Theseus and the Minotaur,* based on a drawing that Ingres made at Herculaneum (Cleveland, *op. cit.,* p. 232) is clearer here than in other versions.

Since the painting of Stratonice is incomplete, as are details of Antiochus, Seleucus and Erasistratus, one assumes that Ingres abandoned this first idea in favor of his later composition.

*The Cleveland Museum of Art*

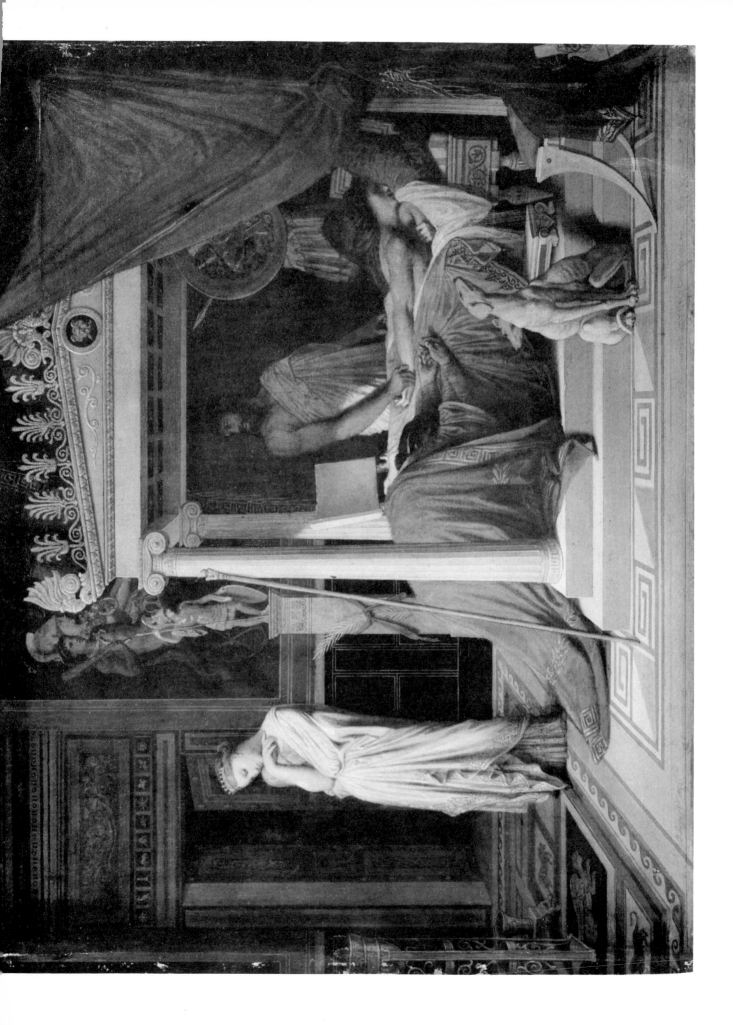

Soft graphite and black chalk over stylus contours on heavy, cream-colored laid paper, partially squared for transfer. 19⅜ x 12⅝ in. (492 x 321 mm.)

Signed in black chalk at the lower left: *Ingres.*

Red stamp of the E.-F. Haro Collection (L. 1241) at the lower left.

CONDITION:    The heavy laid paper of the type which Ingres often used for his compositional studies contains impurities which have discolored with age. The drawing has not been bleached.

PROVENANCE:    Étienne-François Haro; Jan Heyligers, Rotterdam; purchased by the Metropolitan Museum of Art in Paris, 1963.

BIBLIOGRAPHY:    *Un Choix de dessins de Jean-Dominique Ingres,* Paris, 1926, no. 333, reprod. (wrongly said to belong to the Musée Ingres, Montauban); Alazard, 1950, pl. LXXI; Jacob Bean, *100 European Drawings in the Metropolitan Museum of Art,* New York, 1964, no. 66, reprod.

EXHIBITIONS:    Paris, 1867, no. 192.

As Jacob Bean has pointed out (*op. cit.*), this magnificent, virtually full-scale study is closely related to the figure of Stratonice in the Chantilly painting. In no other version of *Antiochus and Stratonice* is the correspondence in pose and dress as exact. For example, in the Cleveland oil sketch (No. 78) the drapery is of a different length and weight. A replica of the Chantilly painting, executed in 1860 on paper appliqued to canvas, differs both in scale and in details of the composition (R. M. de Schauensee Collection, Philadelphia). Perhaps the most striking change is the addition of a pair of greyhounds in the foreground. In the de Schauensee version Stratonice wears a diadem as she does in the draped figure from the National Gallery of Scotland. In a final repetition of the theme, painted in 1866 and now at Montpellier, the composition has been reversed. There are more than twenty drawings of Stratonice preserved in various museums, the majority at Montauban.

An echo of the pose, which recalls antique sources, occurs in the *Portrait of Madame d'Haussonville* (Frick Collection, New York).

*The Metropolitan Museum of Art,*
*Gustavus A. Pfeiffer Fund, 1963*

Ingres à
Madame Gonin
flor 1841.

Ingres à son Excellent ami M. Gonin
Nov. 1841.

Graphite on white paper. Sight measurements: 10 x 7⅜ in. (252 x 187 mm.)*

Signed at the lower left: *Ingres à* | *Madame Gonin* | *flor. 1841*

PROVENANCE:     Mme. Jean-Pierre Gonin, née Louise Lafon (d. 1858); her daughter Mme. Auguste Guerber, née Louise Gonin (d. 1892); her son, Arnold Guerber (d. 1911); his daughter, Miss Hélène A. Guerber (d. 1929); her nephew, Roger S. Guerber.

BIBLIOGRAPHY:     Tony André, *L'Eglise évangélique réformée de Florence depuis son origine jusqu'à nos jours,* Florence, 1899, reprod. opp. p. 44; Lapauze, 1911, p. 213 (reference to family), reprod. p. 363; Louise Guerber, "Three Portraits by Ingres," *Bulletin of the Metropolitan Museum of Art,* XXII, August, 1927, p. 215; Zabel, 1930, p. 436; Louise Guerber Burroughs, "Ingres in Florence," *Creative Art,* X, May, 1932, pp. 364-68, reprod. p. 364; Walter Pach, *Ingres,* New York and London, 1939, p. 26; Hans Naef, "Ingres als Portraitist seiner Westschweizerischen Freunde," *Du,* XV, August, 1955, p. 17, fig. 2; Hans Naef and Louise Burroughs, "Ingres et les familles Gonin, Thomeguex et Guerber," *Genava,* n.s., XIV, Fall, 1966, no. 16.

EXHIBITIONS:     Springfield, etc., 1939-40, no. 35; New York, 1961, no. 50, reprod.

In 1841 on his way back to Paris from Rome where he had completed his term as Director of the French Academy, Ingres and his wife again stopped in Florence and visited their friends of the family Guerber-Thomeguex. It was the last time he saw them. Curiously enough, although at one time or another he had made some twenty portrait drawings of various members of the family, it was only during this last visit of 1841 that he drew the likenesses of the two who were his dearest friends. As he himself had expressed it in a letter to his wife in 1824, "si bons et bons et bons amis" (Lapauze, 1910, p. 276), and he requests her to embrace them for him, those dear friends whose equal he could not hope to find even in Paris.

Jean-Pierre Gonin, represented here, was born in Geneva in 1783. Thus he was three years Ingres' junior and is shown here at the age of fifty-eight. He had begun his career in Geneva as a clerk in the great Bernese merchant house of Guerber. About 1815 he was sent to Florence by the Guerbers to open a branch there. The Florentine venture prospered, and within a short time he was made a member of the firm which then became the Guerber-Gonin Company. His first three children had been born in Geneva. Three more were born in Florence.

A devout Protestant, some of whose ancestors had died for their faith, Gonin was one of the moving spirits in founding the Evangelical Church in Florence. His lasting monument is the Protestant cemetery in Florence which his effort brought into being and where he is buried, as is Admiral Fleetwood Pellew (No. 39), Walter Savage Landor and Elizabeth Barrett Browning. He died in 1854, having seen, in his last years, the firm which he founded and made prosper go into bankruptcy. Although Ingres and his wife were Catholics, no religious controversy or difference seems ever to have cast the slightest cloud over their friendship with the Gonin-Guerber family.

*Roger S. Guerber, White Plains, New York*

Graphite. Sight measurements: 10¼ x 8 in. (259 x 203 mm.)

Signed at the lower right: *Ingres à Son Excellent ami M. Gonin | flor. 1841.*

PROVENANCE:   Jean-Pierre Gonin (d. 1854); his widow, née Louise Lafon (d. 1858); Mme. Auguste Guerber, née Louise Gonin (d. 1892); her son Arnold Guerber (d. 1911); his daughter Miss Hélène A. Guerber (d. 1929); her nephew Roger S. Guerber.

BIBLIOGRAPHY:   Lapauze, 1911, p. 213; Louise Guerber, "Three Drawings by Ingres," *Bulletin of the Metropolitan Museum of Art,* August, 1927, p. 215; Zabel, 1930, p. 436; Louise Guerber Burroughs, "Ingres in Florence," *Creative Art,* x, May, 1932, reprod. p. 366; Walter Pach, *Ingres,* New York and London, 1939, p. 26; Hans Naef, "Ingres als Portraitist seiner Westschweizerischen Freunde," *Du,* xv, August, 1955, p. 17, fig. 3; Hans Naef and Louise Burroughs, "Ingres et les familles Gonin, Thomeguex et Guerber," *Genava,* n.s., xiv, Fall, 1966, no. 17.

EXHIBITIONS:   Springfield, etc., 1939-40, no. 36, reprod.; New York, 1961, no. 51, reprod.

Madame Gonin and her husband were born in the same year at Geneva where, in 1809, they were married. A generous, simple woman, she presided over a household known for its warmth and cordiality. The Swiss painter Constantin, who introduced Ingres and his wife into the Gonin-Guerber-Thomeguex circle, wrote of her influence, "C'est une maison d'une ange." After her husband's death in Florence in 1854, she retired to her native Geneva where she died in 1858.

*Roger S. Guerber, White Plains, New York*

Graphite. Sight measurements: 10¼ x 8 in. (261 x 204 mm.)*

Signed at the lower left: *Ingres à | Madame Guerber | flor 1841.*

PROVENANCE:   Mme. Auguste Guerber, née Louise Gonin (d. 1892); her son Arnold Guerber (d. 1911); his daughter Miss Hélène A. Guerber (d. 1929); her nephew Roger S. Guerber.

BIBLIOGRAPHY:   Lapauze, 1911, p. 213; Louise Guerber, "Three Drawings by Ingres," *Bulletin of the Metropolitan Museum of Art,* August, 1927, p. 215; Zabel, 1930, p. 436; Louise Guerber Burroughs, "Ingres in Florence," *Creative Art,* x, May, 1932, reprod. p. 367; Walter Pach, *Ingres,* New York and London, 1939, p. 26; Hans Naef, "Ingres als Portraitist seiner Westschweizerischen Freunde," *Du,* xv, August, 1955, p. 18, fig. 4; Hans Naef and Louise Burroughs, "Ingres et les familles Gonin, Thomeguex et Guerber," *Genava,* n.s., xiv, Fall, 1966, no. 18.

EXHIBITIONS:   Springfield, etc., 1939-40, no. 34.

Samuel-Auguste Guerber was the son-in-law of Jean-Pierre Gonin (No. 80). M. Gonin had received his first job from Samuel Gottlieb Guerber, Auguste's father; and later, in Florence, his daughter Louise became the young man's wife. Samuel Gottlieb Guerber died in 1837. Therefore in 1841, when this portrait was drawn, the sitter, as his father's eldest son, had become the head of the family. He seems to have borne his duties with ease and grace, and, at the moment of posing, to have regarded the artist who was sketching him with an expression of slightly amused and affectionate tolerance.

He left Florence for America in 1844. A year later his numerous family followed him, and they settled in Bay Ridge, New York, where he died in 1863. The drawing is lent by his grandson.

*Roger S. Guerber, White Plains, New York*

Ingres à
Madame Guerber
f[?] 1841.

Soft graphite on white wove paper. 11¾ x 9⅛ in. (300 x 230 mm.)

Signed at the lower right: *Ingres à son jeune | ami M. Gounod | Rom 1841.*

Inscribed on the score at the left: *DON | JUAN | de | MOZART.*

CONDITION:     The paper is slightly yellowed and has suffered minor stains, now minimized by chalk.

PROVENANCE:     Charles Gounod (d. 1893); Mme. Charles Gounod, née Anna Zimmerman (d. 1906); their daughter Jeanne, la Baronne Pierre de Lassus Saint-Geniès, to Paul Brame, Paris, 1942; César de Hauke to Mrs. Chauncey McCormick.

REPRODUCTIONS: Engraved by Jean-Alexandre Coraboeuf (Salon, 1934).

BIBLIOGRAPHY:     Edmond Saglio, "Un nouveau tableau de M. Ingres, Liste complète de ses oeuvres," *La correspondence littéraire,* 5 February 1857, p. 79; Philippe de Chennevières, "Souvenirs d'un directeur des Beaux-Arts," *L'Artiste* (offprint), 1886, p. 93; Ernest Hébert, "La Villa Médicis en 1840, souvenirs d'un pensionnaire," *Gazette des Beaux-Arts,* xxv, 1 April 1901, p. 271, reprod.; Lapauze, 1903, pp. 20, 24 ff., 26, no. 27, reprod.; Lapauze, 1911, pp. 346, 357, reprod. p. 368; Charles Saunier, "Exposition Ingres," *Les Arts,* x, July, 1911, p. 28; Lili Frölich-Bum, *Ingres,* Vienna and Leipzig, 1924, p. 24, pl. 51; Henry Lapauze, *Histoire de l'Académie de France à Rome,* Paris, 1924, II, p. 255; Louis Hourticq, *Ingres,* Paris, 1928, p. 82, detail reprod.; Morton D. Zabel, "The Portrait Methods of Ingres," *Art and Archaeology,* XXVIII, October, 1929, p. 111; Jean-Paul Alaux, *Académie de France à Rome,* Paris, 1933, II, p. 175, reprod.; Miller, 1938, pp. 11, 13, fig. 8; Pierre Courthion, *Ingres raconté par lui-même et par ses amis,* Geneva, 1947, I, reprod. opp. p. 209; Alazard, 1950, p. 93; for the complete bibliography, including biographical literature, see Hans Naef, "Portrait Drawings by Ingres in the Art Institute of Chicago," *Museum Studies,* I, Winter, 1966, pp. 66-83.

EXHIBITIONS:     Paris, Grand Palais, 1900, *Exposition centennale de l'art français, 1800-1900,* no. 1089; Paris, Grand Palais, 1905, Salon d'automne, *Ingres Retrospective,* no. 63; Paris, Palais du Domaine de Bagatelle, 1908, *Portraits d'hommes et de femmes célèbres,* no. 105, reprod.; Paris, Musée des Arts décoratifs, 1934, *Les artistes français en Italie de Poussin à Renoir,* no. 544; Rotterdam, Paris, New York, 1958-59, no. 133, pl. 107.

The drawing was made in Rome between 13 February and 6 April 1841. The young Gounod, winner of the *Prix de Rome* for music in 1839, arrived at the Villa Medici in January, 1840, when Ingres was still Director. Ingres, who had known Gounod's father, a painter of talent, recognized the son even before the latter had time to give his name. The mature painter was delighted to have someone whose devotion to music more than equaled his own. There followed many happy occasions when the young Gounod played the piano and sang, and the painter accompanied on the violin. Ingres also discovered that the young Gounod could draw as well as his father. He had the musician make many tracings for him after engravings of "the primitives." Some of the most perceptive and sympathetic criticism of Ingres was written by Charles Gounod (see Naef, *op. cit.*).

When the young Charles had set out from Paris for Rome, his adoring yet wise mother, a widow since Charles was five who had done everything she could to foster his career, gave him as a parting gift the score of Mozart's *Don Giovanni.* For Ingres this was the greatest music ever written. He has depicted his young colleague seated at the piano with the score of *Don Giovanni* open on the music rack. The drawing was made as a farewell gift by Ingres when his term as Director was at a close. He presented it to Gounod before his departure. However, since Gounod was going to Germany and Austria for another year, Ingres took it with him to Paris and presented it to Gounod's mother.

*The Art Institute of Chicago,*
*Gift of Messrs. Charles Deering McCormick,*
*Brooks McCormick and Roger McCormick, 1964*

DON
JUAN
de
Mozart

Ingres à son jeune
ami M. Gounod
Rom 1841

Graphite accented with charcoal, stumped and heightened with white chalk (now largely effaced), on tracing paper which has been affixed to cream-colored laid paper. 7⅞ x 9⅞ in. (189 x 239 mm.)

Signed at the lower right: *Ing.*

Inscribed by the artist at the lower left: *Main de M⁹ⁿᵉᵘʳ le Duc d'Orleans.*

Red stamp of the E.-F. Haro Collection at the lower right (L. 1241).

PROVENANCE: Etienne-François Haro; Thibaudeau; Henri Lehman (Sale, Paris, Hôtel Drouot, 2-3 March 1883, no. 201); Comtesse de Béhague; Comtesse de Béarn; acquired by Grenville L. Winthrop in 1931.

BIBLIOGRAPHY: Galichon, 1861, p. 356; Lapauze, 1911, pp. 370 ff., reprod. p. 382; Mongan, 1944, pp. 402-03; Georges Wildenstein, "Les Portraits du Duc d'Orléans par Ingres," *Gazette des Beaux-Arts,* XLVIII, November, 1956, p. 77; Martin Davies, *National Gallery Catalogues, French School,* London, 1957, pp. 113-14, fn. 17; Ternois, 1959, cited above, no. 160.

EXHIBITIONS: Paris, 1861; Paris, 1867, no. 234.

Ferdinand-Philippe, Duc d'Orléans, born at Palermo in 1810, was the eldest son of Louis Philippe and Marie-Amélie. After a brief career, both as a distinguished soldier and as a sensitive, enthusiastic collector of the art of his own day, he died on 19 July 1842, the victim of a carriage accident at Neuilly.

The handsome young Duc d'Orléans was a great admirer of Ingres. He waited until the artist returned from Rome in 1841 before commissioning an official portrait. Although Ingres protested that he did not want to do more portraits, he could not resist the young prince. The canvas was begun late in November, 1841. It was delivered, framed, on 6 May 1842, a little more than two months before the unfortunate accident claimed the life of the duke. That portrait still belongs to the family (Wildenstein, pl. 90). Ingres repeated the portrait, introducing variations in scale, setting, and even costume. Some replicas were for the family. Five others were made in Ingres' studio for various cities of France at the request of the government, with Ingres retouching his students' work.

The Ingres Museum at Montauban has seven preparatory studies. Four show the artist searching for an acceptable pose. In two of these sketches the young duke faces slightly left. In another study, knee length, frontal and with the left hand on the hip (Ternois, no. 162), the right hand holds the cocked hat and his gloves. Here the fingers of the glove show between his thumb and first finger exactly as they do in this drawing. The sleeve, buttons, and the angle of the hand are similar in the finished portrait, but there the gloves have been reversed so that the fingers point down and the thumb is caught into the belt, with the hat held in the crook of the arm. Therefore this drawing, although it is on tracing paper and of natural size, was not the final solution for the finished portrait. Another drawing of the hand was given to the École des Beaux-Arts by Gatteaux.

*Fogg Art Museum, Harvard University,*
*Bequest of Grenville L. Winthrop, 1943.852*

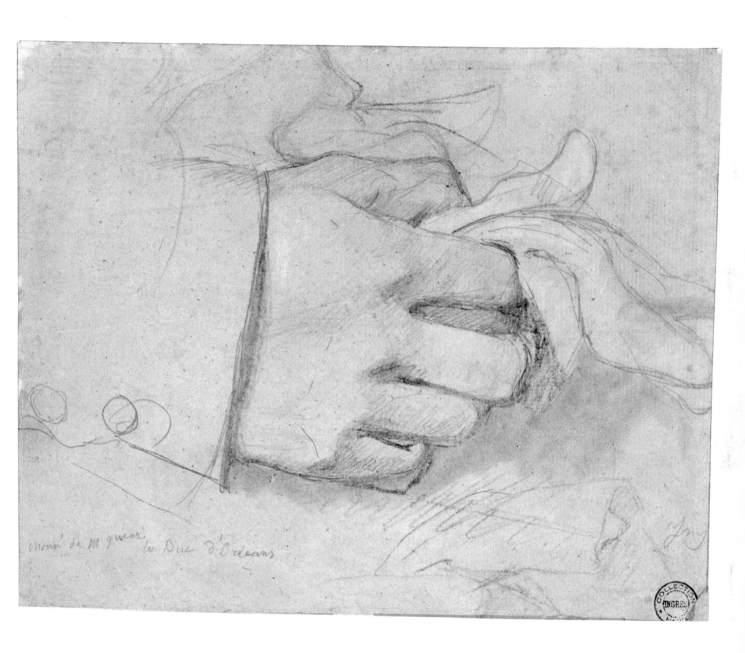

Mains de M<sup>r</sup> guerin le Duc d'Orléans

Graphite on thin white wove paper, squared for transfer. $9\frac{3}{16}$ x $7\frac{3}{4}$ in. (234 x 196 mm.)*

Signed at the lower left: *Ing*

CONDITION:     The upper left corner has been replaced with Japanese rice paper, and a very small hole in the skirt, beneath the sitter's right forearm, has been patched. Although the paper was thinned from the back when it was removed from an old mount, the surface was not disturbed.

PROVENANCE:    Alfred Beurdeley (Sale, Paris, Georges Petit Gallery, 2 December 1920, no. 242); Wildenstein to Paul J. Sachs, 1927.

BIBLIOGRAPHY:  Andrew Ritchie, "The Evolution of Ingres' Portrait of the Comtesse d'Haussonville," *Art Bulletin,* XXII, September, 1940, pp. 120-26, reprod. fig. 8; Mongan-Sachs, 1940, no. 704, fig. 375; Agnes Mongan, *The Frick Collection: French Pictures,* Pittsburgh, 1949, I, p. 199; Alazard, 1950, pl. LXXXIX; Shoolman-Slatkin, 1950, p. 18, reprod. pl. 66; James Watrous, *The Craft of Old Master Drawings,* Madison, Wisconsin, 1957, p. 122, reprod. p. 137; Ternois, 1959, above no. 64.

EXHIBITIONS:   St. Petersburgh, 1912, *Exposition Centennale de l'art français,* no. 664; Cambridge, 1929, no. 86; Springfield, etc., 1939-40, no. 45; Chicago, Minneapolis, Detroit, San Francisco, 1955-56, *Musées de France, Travelling Exhibition of French Drawings,* no. 107, pp. 46-47; Bloomington, Indiana University, 1957, *Baudelaire and the Graphic Arts,* p. 7, reprod.; Rotterdam, Paris, New York, 1958-59, no. 135, pl. 108; New York, 1961, no. 55, reprod.; Cambridge, Fogg Art Museum, 1965-66, *Memorial Exhibition, Works of Art from the Collection of Paul J. Sachs,* no. 45, reprod.

Mme. d'Haussonville (1818-82), née Louise de Broglie, was the granddaughter of Mme. de Stael and the great-granddaughter of Necker. In 1836 she married the Vicomte Othenin d'Haussonville, deputy, senator, historian, and member of the French Academy. In later years, she turned to writing and published an historical novel, *Robert Emmet,* 1858, and two biographies, *Marguerite de Valois,* 1870, and *Les Dernières Années de Lord Byron,* 1874.

Ingres accepted the commission for her portrait in 1842 and in that year painted a preliminary oil sketch (Wildenstein, no. 238) for an oval portrait, facing to the right. During the following three years, Ingres continued to work on the portrait; but he abandoned his original plan and began extensive studies on a new composition which culminated in the elaborate and beautifully detailed portrait finished in 1845, now in the Frick Collection.

For the final composition Ingres reversed the Vicomtesse's pose, and placed her in front of a small fireplace with a velvet valance and curtains and a garniture of vases in front of a mirror which reflects her image. Almost two dozen drawings exist, practically half of which are at Montauban, testifying to Ingres' thoroughness and his demand for perfection in preparing the portrait. In this study he is concerned with the spatial arrangement of the figure and the angular placement of the console and mirror. Her pose is very close to that in the finished portrait but without much of the formal restraint which characterizes the painted version.

*Fogg Art Museum, Harvard University,*
*Bequest of Meta and Paul J. Sachs, 1965.294*

Charcoal over graphite on thin white wove paper. 14⅛ x 8⅛ in. (359 x 204 mm.)

Inscribed to the right of the figure: *plus de mouvement* | *grand foyer de* | *lumiere* | *plus* (crossed out).

Turquoise stamp of the Ingres Sale at the lower right (L. 1477).

CONDITION: An old horizontal crease 5¼ in. from the top edge has been flattened. An ⅛-in. hole above the flounce in the skirt has been patched.

PROVENANCE: M. Ernst May; Alphonse Kann to Paul J. Sachs, 1920.

BIBLIOGRAPHY: Andrew C. Ritchie, "The Evolution of Ingres' Portrait of the Comtesse d'Haussonville," *Art Bulletin,* XXII, September, 1940, p. 123, fig. 10; Mongan-Sachs, 1940, no. 705, fig. 376; Alazard, 1950, pl. LXXVIII; James Watrous, *The Craft of Old Master Drawings,* Madison, Wisconsin, 1956, reprod. p. 131; Ternois, 1959, above no. 64; Jacob Rosenberg, *Great Draughtsmen from Pisanello to Picasso,* Cambridge, 1959, p. XXII, reprod. 195b.

EXHIBITIONS: Cambridge, 1929, no. 88; New York, 1961, no. 56, reprod.; Cambridge, Fogg Art Museum, 1965-66, *Memorial Exhibition, Works of Art from the Collection of Paul J. Sachs,* no. 46, reprod.

Except for the scarf which she clutches around her shoulders, Mme. d'Haussonville is in the same dress and pose as the finished portrait. The scarf was abandoned, but other details of this drawing, including the position of her fingers, were retained. Related studies include a very similar drawing in the Frick Collection, several sketches at Montauban (Ternois, 1959, nos. 66, 67 and 69) and another in the collection of the British Museum.

*Fogg Art Museum, Harvard University,*
*Bequest of Meta and Paul J. Sachs, 1965.295*

plus de mouvement

grand foyer de
lumière
peut

Stylus lines over graphite on very thin white wove paper which had been affixed to heavy wove paper. Lightly squared for transfer in graphite. $16\frac{3}{8}$ x $12\frac{7}{16}$ in. (416 x 315 mm.)

Watermark: LA * F & G.

Inscribed to the right of the woman's knee: *cuisses un peu longues.*

Signed at the lower right: *Ingres*

Red stamp of the E. F. Haro Collection at the lower left (L. 1241).

CONDITION:    The design area is very slightly discolored as a result of age and exposure to light. The edges have been seriously stained by the wood-pulp window within which the drawing was formerly mounted.

PROVENANCE:    E. F. Haro; Martin Birnbaum to Grenville L. Winthrop, 1936.

BIBLIOGRAPHY:    Blanc, 1870, p. 242; Mongan, 1947, no. 20, reprod.; Shoolman-Slatkin, 1950, p. 122, pl. 68; Kenneth Clark, *The Nude*, 1956, p. 159, no. 116, reprod.; Paul J. Sachs, *The Pocket Book of Great Drawings*, New York, 1951, reprod.; Mongan, 1962, no. 723, reprod.

EXHIBITIONS:    Paris, 1867.

These two classical figures, among the most memorable of all Ingres drawings of the nude, were made when Ingres was designing his great wall decoration *The Golden Age*. As his program progressed, they underwent many changes of pose and position. As a result, the figures are scarcely recognizable in the painting itself. One can follow their gradual metamorphosis in the more than four hundred surviving studies for the composition, the majority now in the collection at Montauban.

It was in September, 1837, that the Duc de Luynes commissioned Ingres to paint a series of murals representing The Four Ages of the World at the Château de Dampierre (Chevreuse). Ingres did not begin work until 1843. Although he read widely, primarily Ovid, and made a great many studies, the work advanced slowly. Finally in March, 1850, with the Duke's agreement, Ingres withdrew from the project. The *Golden Age* was incomplete, the *Age of Iron* scarcely begun, and thus they remained.

In 1862 Ingres signed and dated a small, completed replica on panel of the large painting. That replica also came to the Fogg Museum in the Winthrop Bequest.

The program of the painting, that is, the literary and artistic sources, and its iconography have been carefully worked out. The reasons for the many changes have been examined. If the literary sources (Hesiod and Ovid) are clear, the pictorial sources are complex, the changes gradual and fascinating. It is hoped that two recent studies of this material, one by Gail Davidson, will soon be published.

*Fogg Art Museum, Harvard University,*
*Bequest of Grenville L. Winthrop, 1943.861*

Graphite heightened with white chalk. 12½ x 9⅛ in. (318 x 232 mm.)

Signed at the lower right: *J. Ingres Del. | à Madame Reiset | Enghien 1844.*

PROVENANCE:  Mme. Frédéric Reiset, the sitter's daughter, to her husband F. Reiset (d. 1891); to their daughter, Comtesse de Ségur-Lamoignon (d. 1899); to her son le Comte de Ségur-Lamoignon; Wildenstein to Mr. and Mrs. John W. Warrington.

BIBLIOGRAPHY:  Galichon, 1861, p. 361; Delaborde, 1870, no. 404; Philippe de Chennevières, *Souvenirs d'un Directeur des Beaux-Arts,* Paris, 1886, 3rd ed., pp. 91, 94; Charles Saunier, "Exposition Ingres," *Les Arts,* no. 115, July, 1911, reprod. p. 28; Brinsley Ford, "Ingres' Portraits of the Reiset Family," *Burlington Magazine,* xcv, November, 1953, p. 359, fig. 11, p. 357.

EXHIBITIONS:  Paris, 1861, no. 72; Paris, 1911, no. 156; Paris, 1921, no. 112; New Haven, Yale University Art Gallery, 1956, *Pictures Collected by Yale Alumni,* no. 208, reprod.; Rotterdam, Paris, New York, 1958-59, no. 134, pl. 103; New York, 1961, no. 59, reprod.

Louis-Xavier Reiset was born at Colmar in 1779. He died in Paris in 1852. A lieutenant of the Dragoons of the Imperial Guard, he was created Officer of the Legion of Honor, 19 February 1814. Two years later he was retired with the rank of captain. He is the father of Augustine-Modeste-Hortense Reiset whose portrait painted by Ingres in 1844 is in the Fogg Museum. (His son-in-law, Frédéric, a famous curator of the Louvre, was also his nephew.)

It was at Enghien in 1844 that Ingres drew this portrait, as well as the one of his son-in-law (Brinsley Ford Collection, London), Madame Reiset (also Brinsley Ford Collection, London) the second portrait of Madame Reiset with her little daughter (Boymans-van Beuningen Museum, Rotterdam). In 1850 Ingres drew another portrait of Mademoiselle Reiset (Mrs. Douglas Williams Collection, New York), No. 94 of the present exhibition. After the death of his first wife, Ingres had withdrawn for a time to the Reisets' hospitable country home.

*Mr. and Mrs. John N. Warrington, Cincinnati*

J. Ingres del.
à Madame Reiset
Enghien 1844

Oil (limited palette of browns and flesh tones) on canvas. 16 x 12⅞ in. (406 x 327 mm.)

Signed at the lower right: *Ingres à Madame Cavé*

PROVENANCE:     Mme. Edmond Cavé, Paris; Albert Boulanger-Cavé (until 1911); Gaston LeRoy (Sale, Paris, Hôtel Drouot, 19-20 May 1926, no. 53) to Paul Rosenberg, Paris and New York; C. Chauncey Stillman, New York (Sale, New York, American Art Association, 3 February 1927, no. 10); Paul Rosenberg, New York, to Grace Rainey Rogers, New York, 1927.

BIBLIOGRAPHY:     Lapauze, 1911, p. 386, reprod. p. 389; Lili Fröhlich-Bum, *Ingres, sein Leben und sein Stil,* Vienna and Leipzig, 1924, p. 26; *Bulletin de la Revue de l'art ancien et moderne,* 1926, pp. 232 ff., reprod.; Louis Hourticq, *Ingres,* Paris, 1928, p. 89, reprod.; A. Joubin, "Deux amies de Delacroix: Mme. Elisabeth Boulanger-Cavé et Mme. Rang-Babut," *Revue de l'art ancien et moderne,* LVII, 1930, pp. 60 ff., reprod.; Wildenstein, 1954, p. 216, no. 247, pl. 94; *Catalogue of French Paintings II,* Metropolitan Museum of Art, pp. 12-13, reprod., to be published; Frank Trapp, "A Mistress and a Master: Mme. Cavé and Delacroix," to be published.

EXHIBITIONS:     Paris, 1911, no. 47; New York, 1961, no. 58, reprod.

Marie-Elisabeth Blavot married Edmond Cavé in 1844, the year in which this and the following sketch were executed. She was born in Paris in 1810. An artist of distinction in her own right, she studied watercolor under Roqueplan and painting with Clément Boulanger, a pupil of Ingres and her cousin. She married him in 1831. She exhibited at the Salon from 1835 or 1836 until 1855. In 1838 she accompanied Delacroix to Belgium and Holland, a journey which has been described by Escholier (*Delacroix,* Paris, 1926-29, 3 vols., II, pp. 255 ff.) and which will be discussed further by Frank Trapp (forthcoming number of the *Art Journal*). Boulanger died in 1842. Two years later his widow married Cavé.

A woman of many gifts and great intelligence, Mme. Cavé was also a writer of considerable influence. Her little volume *Le dessin sans maître* first appeared in Paris in 1850; further editions appeared in 1851, 1852 and 1857. It was translated into English as *Drawing without a Master,* and published in New York in 1868. *L'Aquarelle sans maître* appeared in 1851 (translated into English as *Color,* New York, 1882). The "Cavé method" became a familiar term in the mid-nineteenth century. Delacroix, who had strongly influenced her theories and whose friendship and admiration for her were known, reviewed both her books in the *Revue de deux mondes,* 15 September 1850.

Madame Cavé had the unusual distinction of being a good friend of both Delacroix and Ingres. That both painters admired her beauty as well as her talents is clear. Delacroix drew a pastel portrait of her in 1856, now in the Daber Collection, Paris (Sale catalogue, Paris, Galérie Charpentier, 3 December 1957, reprod. no. 83). In her book *Color,* she specifically referred to this portrait by Ingres, mentioning it as an example of a rough draft in oils. "My profile made by M. Ingres would be a draft; he made it in an hour, and, nevertheless, it is one of his masterpieces.'

*The Metropolitan Museum of Art,*
*Bequest of Grace Rainey Rogers, 1943*

Ingres à Madame Cavé

Oil on canvas. 16 x 12⅞ in. (407 x 327 mm.)

Signed at the lower right: *Ingres a Madame | Cavé — 1844.*

PROVENANCE:    Mme. Edmond Cavé, Paris; Albert Boulanger-Cavé (until 1911); Gaston Le Roy (Sale, Paris, Hôtel Drouot, 19-20 May 1926, no. 34, reprod.) to Paul Rosenberg, Paris and New York; Grace Rainey Rogers, New York, 1926.

BIBLIOGRAPHY:    Lapauze, 1911, p. 386, reprod. p. 375; L. Fröhlich-Bum, *Ingres, sein Leben und sein Stil,* Vienna and Leipzig, 1924, p. 26; *Bulletin de l'art ancien et moderne,* 1926, pp. 232 ff., reprod.; Louis Hourticq, *Ingres,* Paris, 1928, p. 89, reprod.; M. Malingue, *Ingres,* Paris, 1943, reprod. p. 51; Alazard, 1950, p. 106; Wildenstein, 1954, p. 214, no. 246, pl. 95; Ternois, 1959, cited above, no. 20; *Catalogue of French Paintings II,* Metropolitan Museum of Art, pp. 11-12, reprod. p. 12, to be published.

EXHIBITIONS:    Paris, 1911, no. 46; New York, 1961, no. 57, reprod.

Edmond-Ludovic (or Hygin)-Auguste Cavé (1794-1852) was a writer of vaudeville sketches who, in 1839, became the Director of Fine Arts under the Minister of the Interior. He held the position until the Revolution in 1848, when he was supplanted by Charles Blanc, the founder and first editor of the *Gazette des Beaux-Arts.* M. Cavé, like his wife, was a friend and admirer of both Delacroix and Ingres.

There is a drawing of M. Cavé in black crayon in the museum at Montauban which corresponds in scale to the Metropolitan oil sketch. Momméja considered the Montauban drawing a replica, but Ternois (*op. cit.*) notes that the contours show signs of having been traced with a sharp point. Because of this evidence he believes that the Montauban sketch was the original study and was transferred to the canvas by Ingres as a first step. Crayon portrait drawings by Ingres are rare.

The two Cavé portraits were probably drawn by Ingres as wedding gifts.

*The Metropolitan Museum of Art,*
*Bequest of Grace Rainey Rogers, 1943*

Yngres à Madame
Cavè.
1844

Graphite. 12⅛ x 9½ in. (323 x 243 mm.)

Signed at the lower left: *Ingres Del.* | *à Monsieur* | *henri Gonze.* Dated at the lower right: *mars 22. 1845*

CONDITION:      The drawing is exceptionally well preserved. Its original tablet, now mounted behind the drawing, measures 325 x 245 mm.

PROVENANCE:     Madame Gonse (d. 1901) to her son Félix-Henri-Marie-René Gonse, a flower painter; his widow, later Madame Bradberry, to Henry Lapauze in 1910; Lapauze Sale, Paris, Hôtel Drouot, 21 June 1929, to Paul Rosenberg; Wildenstein, New York, to Mrs. Albert Lasker.

BIBLIOGRAPHY:    Lapauze, 1911, reprod. p. 395; Frank Elgar, *Ingres*, Paris, 1951, fig. 75, p. 12.

EXHIBITIONS:     Paris, 1911, no. 158; Paris, Palais des Beaux-Arts, 1913, *David et ses élèves*, no. 358; Copenhagen, Statens Museum for Kunst, 1914, *Art français du XIXᵉ siècle*, no. 296; London, Wildenstein, 1934, *French Drawings from Clouet to Ingres*, no. 53, pl. XVI; New York, Wildenstein, 1947-48, *French XIX Century Drawings,* no. 30; Paris, André Weil Gallery, *Ingres,* no. 61; New York, 1961, no. 61, reprod.

The daughter of a French deputy, Joséphine-Caroline Maille was born 7 February 1815 in Rouen. Her friendship with Ingres and his wife was presumably of long standing. Her father had been a close friend of the artist. In 1834, it was he who supervised the installation of the *Martyrdom of S. Symphorien* at Autun. A portrait of Mme. Ingres inscribed "à Mademoiselle Maille" and dated March, 1835, is preserved at Montauban. Mlle. Maille herself painted and, according to Lapauze (1911, p. 452), Ingres advised her in her work.

In 1845, after her marriage to Jean-Henri Gonse, *conseiller à la cour d'appel de Rouen,* Ingres began a portrait of Mme. Gonse. The project, which continued for seven years, can be followed in the many charming letters written to Mme. Gonse by Ingres and later published by Lapauze (*op. cit.*). Mrs. Lasker's drawing, dated 22 March 1845, was undoubtedly executed at the time Ingres began his work on the canvas. The latter, now in the collection at Montauban, was seen by many Americans in an exhibition which traveled to museums throughout the United States in 1952-53.

*Mrs. Albert D. Lasker, New York*

Ingres Del.
à Monsieur
henri Gonse.

Mars 22. 1845.

Pen and ink (recto) with graphite (verso) on tracing paper, now mounted on blue wove paper. 11⅞ x 15⅜ in. (302 x 392 mm.)

Inscribed by Raymond Balze along the base of the altar: *ces croquis preparatoire a un tableau | autre que le portrait costumé | du Musée du Louvre.* Inscribed at the lower left: *Dessins pour Le plutarque français.* Inscribed at the lower center: *note de R. Balze.*

PROVENANCE:     *Dessins de maîtres anciens et modernes en vente chez R. W. P. de Vries,* Amsterdam, 1929, p. 125, reprod.; Sale, Stuttgart, Stuttgarter Kunstkabinett, 20 May 1953, no. 709.

BIBLIOGRAPHY:     E. Mennechet and I. Hadot, *Le Plutarque français,* second edition, 1844-47, II, p. 141, engraving after Ingres.

The drawing is not, as it seems at first glance, a preparatory study for the painting *Joan of Arc at the Coronation of Charles VII* in the Louvre, a painting which Ingres signed and dated 1854. Although there are resemblances between the sketch and the painting, the drawing precedes the latter by a decade. It is a preliminary study for the drawing of Joan of Arc which Ingres made for the second edition of *Le Plutarque français.* In the second volume of the first edition, published by Edouard Mennechet in Paris, 1835, the illustration for Joan of Arc was based on a drawing by Boilly. Ingres was asked to furnish a design to take the place of the Boilly in the second edition which appeared in 1844. In addition to the Joan of Arc, he furnished drawings of Eustache Le Sueur, Poussin, La Fontaine, Racine and Molière. Preparatory drawings for them all are preserved at Montauban.

The two inscriptions on the drawing, one stating that the study is in preparation for a "tableau" other than the Louvre canvas, and the other, in the hand of Ingres' pupil Raymond Balze, are both accurate. Both must have been added after 1856 when the Louvre painting was finished.

The project throws interesting light on the artist's working methods. A group of early sketches for the design is at Montauban. Not their least interesting aspect is the fact that Ingres first clothed St. Joan in a short, belted, antique tunic, and then in a longer, beltless robe. When the pose was finally determined he studied the figure nude, then in mediaeval armor.

In this drawing, his program had advanced to its final features. Here Ingres drew his figure (the more complete of the two studies, now visible at the right) on the left half of a sheet of tracing paper. He then folded the page, traced the figure in ink (the outline drawing now visible at the left), and opened the page once again. The drawing in graphite at the right is actually on the back of the tracing paper, not on the surface. We see it through the transparent paper, in reverse, facing to the left as the design would appear on the engraver's plate. The figure in ink at the left is the Maid as she appears in the engraving after Ingres' drawing, facing to the right as in the original image.

The outline of a woman's profile, visible if the drawing is turned sideways, is an enlargement of the head of a kneeling woman holding a banner, a drawing which Ingres made in a series of pen and ink copies after details of Durer engravings (Gatteaux, pl. 82).

*Curtis Baer, New York*

ces croquis préparatoires au tableau
autre que le portrait Costume
du Musée du Louvre

Dessins pour le plutarque français        note de R. Balze

Watercolor (lapis blue, violet, vermillion, brown, green and gray) over graphite on tracing paper which has been affixed to white wove paper, varnished and heightened with white gouache. 15⅜ x 13 in. (385 x 330 mm.)

Signed in graphite at the lower left: *J Ingres. inv Del.* Inscribed at the lower right: *Paris 1850 —*

CONDITION:    The varnish has yellowed severely, and two large tears at the upper right have been mended. In two areas the artist used overlays to revise the drawing: a vertical strip one inch in width, behind Virgil, and a large inset at the right. The latter includes the upper half of Augustus' body as well as the two figures behind him. The tracing paper was affixed to the secondary support before the watercolor was executed. Varnish does not cover the overlays or the areas in which white gouache was applied directly or in combination with watercolor.

PROVENANCE:    François Reiset; Reginald Davis, Paris; Grenville L. Winthrop.

BIBLIOGRAPHY:    Galichon, p. 348; Charles Blanc, "Ingres," *Gazette des Beaux-Arts,* XXIII, 1867, p. 199; Delaborde, 1870, no. 194; Mongan, 1944; Agnes Mongan, "Ingres and the Antique," *Journal of the Warburg and Courtauld Institutes,* x, 1947, pp. 9-10, pl. 4a.

This watercolor, which is signed and dated 1850, repeats the carefully calculated floor design and general position of the figures in the Toulouse painting of 1812. Here Ingres has strengthened the composition by the addition of pilasters. Marcellus appears as he did in the Bayonne drawing; Agrippa and Maecenas, in shadow behind Augustus, are clearer than at Toulouse. The watercolor repeats almost every detail of a drawing in the Louvre which Lapauze says was made in 1830 in preparation for Pradier's engraving (Lapauze, 1911, p. 283, reprod.). Since the measurements of the figures vary less than a millimeter one concludes that the basis of the Fogg watercolor was a tracing of the Louvre drawing.

Ingres himself described the composition at length (Delaborde, 1870, pp. 221-23). It is not without significance that he visualized the scene in theatrical terms ("Les acteurs sont. . . ."). If, when he began to work on the theme, Ingres saw Miollis as Maecenas and Napoleon as Agrippa, his own counterpart was the figure of Virgil, the poet of historical drama.

An impression of Pradier's engraving painted to resemble a picture was in the family of Madame Ramel's heirs until the 1950's (Wildenstein, no. 320, fig. 49).

*Fogg Art Museum, Harvard University,*
*Bequest of Grenville L. Winthrop, 1943.373*

Graphite. Sheet: 13⅜ x 9⅝ in. (340 x 245 mm.). Design area framed by double graphite lines (covered by mat): 10⅞ x 7⅜ in. (277 x 187 mm.)*

Signed at the lower right: *Ingres Del.*

PROVENANCE:     The sitter's father Frédéric Reiset (d. 1891); the sitter, Vicomtesse de Ségur-Lamoignon (d. 1899); her daughter la Marquise de Moy; her husband le Marquis de Moy; Gustave Bourgarel (Sale, Paris, 15-16 June 1922, no. 115, reprod. p. 103); Henry Lapauze (Sale, Paris, Hôtel Drouot, 21 June 1929, no. 31, reprod.); Knoedler, New York, to Mrs. Douglas Williams, ca. 1960.

BIBLIOGRAPHY:   Galichon, 1861, p. 361; Delaborde, 1870, no. 408; Lapauze, 1903, no. 82, reprod.; Lapauze, 1911, reprod. p. 428; Brinsley Ford, "Ingres' Portraits of the Reiset Family," *Burlington Magazine,* xcv, November, 1953, p. 356; Ternois, 1959, cited above no. 169.

EXHIBITIONS:    Paris, 1861, no. 71; Paris, 1911, no. 161; Cambridge, Fogg Art Museum, 1934, *French Drawings and Prints of the Nineteenth Century,* no. 48; Springfield, etc., 1939-40, no. 51; Pittsburgh, Carnegie Institute, 1951, *French Painting,* no. 157, reprod.; London, Knoedler Gallery, 1958, *Old Master, Impressionist and Contemporary Drawings,* no. 11; New York, 1961, no. 62, reprod.

Thérèse-Hortense-Marie Reiset was born at Passy in 1836. She first sat for Ingres in 1844, when he drew a double portrait of Marie with her mother. They stand facing the artist, the mother with her arms around the little girl's shoulders, the child with her arms around her mother's skirts (Boymans-van Beuningen Museum, Rotterdam). Two years later, Ingres painted the serenely beautiful portrait of Mme. Reiset which the daughter inherited and which is now in the Fogg Museum. Mme. Reiset, who often received Ingres as a visitor at their country place in Enghien, was gentle and understanding with the sometimes crusty artist. He, on his part, loved the family. These feelings are clearly reflected in his portraits of the Reisets, particularly in the tender and beguiling drawings of mother and daughter.

Although the drawing is not dated, we may rely upon the date 1850 given by Delaborde, for he certainly knew the Reiset family. Marie, as we see her carrying her pet pug dog, is therefore fourteen. Seven years later, she would marry Adolfe-Louis-Edgar de Ségur-Lamoignon, a diplomat. She died in 1899 at her château near Méry, having survived her parents less than a decade (see No. 88, her grandfather).

*Mrs. Douglas Williams, New York*

Black crayon over red chalk. 14⅛ x 12⅞ in. (305 x 235 mm.)

Turquoise stamp of J.-A.-D. Ingres Sale at the lower right (L. 1477).

PROVENANCE:  Ingres atelier; Wildenstein to Worcester Art Museum, 1964.

BIBLIOGRAPHY: Mongan, 1962, no. 724, reprod.; Agnes Mongan, "A Portrait Drawing by Ingres," *Worcester Art Museum News Bulletin and Calendar,* xxx, March, 1965, reprod.

Madame Moitessier was the daughter of M. de Foucault, an important functionary in the Administration of Water and Forests when M. Marcotte was their director. It was through the Marcottes that Ingres met Mme. Moitessier. He had refused to paint her; but when he saw her, he was struck by her beauty and agreed to do a portrait. In the end he painted two, both imposing and unforgettable, one now in the National Gallery, London, the other in the National Gallery, Washington.

This remarkable head, instinct with life, with its calm, appraising gaze, is a study for the London portrait which he began in 1844, but which he only completed in 1856. The agonies, delays, disappointments and final triumph of that portrait are fully documented, as are the remarkable patience and understanding of the sitter (see Martin Davies, "A Portrait by the Aged Ingres," *Burlington Magazine,* LXVIII, June, 1936, pp. 257-68, and A. Mongan, *op. cit.*).

Ingres adapted the pose from a frescoe painting at Herculaneum, now in the Naples Museum. In this drawing he has reversed the head, as he often reversed his figures. Since Madame Moitessier appears here to be somewhat younger than in the finished portrait, we believe the drawing was made before the second version, that is, before 1851.

*Worcester Art Museum,*
*Museum purchase in memory of Mary Alexander*
*Riley with funds given by her friends. 1964*

Graphite on white wove paper. 12½ x 9¼ in. (317 x 235 mm.)

Turquoise stamp of the Ingres Sale at the lower right (L. 1477). Stamp of the Pierre Geismar Collection at the lower left (L. Suppl. 2078[b]).

PROVENANCE:    Fernand Guille, the artist's nephew; M. E. Sylvias; Pierre Geismar (Sale, Paris, 15 November 1928); Jerome Stonborough (Sale, New York, Parke-Bernet Galleries, 17 October 1940, no. 35, reprod.).

BIBLIOGRAPHY:    *Le Figaro,* Monday, 10 December 1877; Agnes Mongan, "Ingres et Madame Moitessier," *Bulletin du Musée Ingres,* no. 2, July, 1957, pp. 3-8, fig. 3.

EXHIBITIONS:    Minneapolis, University of Minnesota, University Gallery, and New York, Solomon R. Guggenheim Museum, 1962, *The Nineteenth Century: One hundred twenty-five Master Drawings,* no. 65.

It seemed that Ingres had reached an impasse and that the portrait of Mme. Moitessier would never be finished. Impatiently he put it to one side. However, after gentle reminders from the patient lady that he had promised her a portrait and that seven years had passed, he suddenly decided on another pose, another dress, another scale. Setting to work with vigor, he completed the Washington portrait within a year.

In this New London drawing, Ingres appears to have decided, after hesitation, upon the pose of the right arm and the design of the dress. The jewelry remains to be selected (the letter in which he asks her to bring it with her to the next sitting has survived), and her coiffure has yet to be elaborated. Here Mme. Moitessier appears less majestic than in the painting, but the squaring indicates that his design is far enough advanced to be transferred to the larger canvas.

A drawing in which the details are less fully developed than in this study, was given by the late Paul Rosenberg to the National Gallery, Washington (Mongan, *op. cit.,* fig. 2). Another version, with the arms in a different position, is in the collection of M. Jacques Dupont, Paris (Lapauze, 1911, reprod. p. 438).

*Lyman Allyn Museum, New London, Connecticut*

Verso: Study for a Figure in "Christ Among the Doctors."

Charcoal over graphite on thin white wove paper, squared in graphite. 7⅜ x 7⅞ in. (187 x 200 mm.)

Turquoise stamp of the Ingres Sale at the lower left (L. 1477).

CONDITION:    The left and lower edges have been abraded.

PROVENANCE:    Charles A. Loeser.

BIBLIOGRAPHY:    Mongan-Sachs, 1940, no. 706; Alazard, 1950, pl. xcv; Agnes Mongan, "Ingres and Madame Moitessier," *Bulletin du Musée Ingres,* no. 2, July, 1957, pp. 3-8, fig. 4; Martin Davies, *National Gallery Catalogue, French School,* National Gallery, London, 1957, p. 124; Ternois, 1959, above no. 124.

When Ingres began the portrait, it was his intention to include Mme. Moitessier's little daughter Catherine at her mother's knees, but the child could not stay still long enough for the painter's demands and was omitted. A drawing at Montauban shows her head (no. 125).

It is difficult to know when this drawing was done, whether it preceded or followed the standing figure of 1851. We surmise that it may have been done about 1851, for the model is wearing if not the same dress, at least a dress with a bodice of the same design.

Free, rather rough position drawings of this kind, in which the artist is blocking out his figure and, as the squaring shows, relating it to his canvas, are not as well known or as numerous as his careful portrait drawings. They make up in vigor and volume what they lose in subtlety. There are four related drawings at Montauban.

*Fogg Art Museum, Harvard University,*
*Bequest of Charles A. Loeser, 1932.178*

J. Ingres Del 1852
à sa bonne famille Raoul

Soft graphite heightened with white chalk on brown wove paper which has been affixed to cream-colored wove paper. 12⅝ x 10⅛ in. (321 x 254 mm.) Very irregular.

Signed at the lower left: *J. Ingres Del | à Sa bonne | famille Ramel | 1852*

CONDITION:    The paper has darkened and has been stained, primarily along the right and lower edges, by a former mount. With the exception of the top, the edges of the original sheet are ragged.

PROVENANCE:    M. and Mme. Ramel, presumably to their daughter, Madame Ingres (d. 1887); to her brother and sole heir, Albert Ramel (d. 1907); to his widow, née Elizabeth Dalloz; Jacques Seligman, New York, to Grenville L. Winthrop, 1927.

BIBLIOGRAPHY:    Delaborde, 1870, no. 394; Blanc, 1870, p. 239; Lapauze, 1903, no. 79, reprod.; Lapauze, 1911, reprod. p. 451; Lili Fröhlich-Bum, *Ingres*, Vienna and Leipzig, 1924, pl. 61; Zabel, 1930, p. 382, reprod. p. 372; Miller, 1938, pp. 14 and 15, reprod. p. 11; Mongan, 1944, p. 400, reprod.; Mongan, 1947, no. 22, reprod.; Alazard, 1950, p. 107, pl. xci.

EXHIBITIONS:    Paris, 1867, no. 384.

Jean-Baptiste-Joseph-Dominique Ramel, born in 1777 at Montolieu (L'Aude), was the Mortgage Commissioner of Versailles. On 27 February 1808, in Paris, he married Delphine Bochet (No. 99). He was therefore a hearty seventy-five when his son-in-law, only three years his junior, drew this portrait. The year was 1852, the year in which Ingres married the first born of their six children, who had been named after her mother. One glance at the expression in the face of this solid and amiable figure is enough to show that the two men shared a deep and affectionate understanding of one another.

*Fogg Art Museum, Harvard University,*
*Bequest of Grenville L. Winthrop, 1943.838*

Soft graphite heightened with white chalk on brown wove paper which has been affixed to cream-colored wove paper. 12$\frac{15}{16}$ x 10⅝ in. (328 x 270 mm.)

Signed at the lower right: *J. Ingres Del 1852* | *à Sa bonne famille Ramel*

CONDITION: The paper is ragged along the left and bottom edges and has darkened with age and exposure to light. It has suffered minor abrasions at the upper right as well as minimal staining near the edges, produced by a former mount.

PROVENANCE: M. and Mme. Ramel, presumably to their daughter, Mme. Ingres (d. 1887); her brother and sole heir, Albert Ramel (d. 1907); his widow, née Elizabeth Dalloz; Jacques Seligman, New York, to Grenville L. Winthrop, 1927.

BIBLIOGRAPHY: Delaborde, 1870, p. 310, no. 395; Blanc, 1870, p. 239; Lapauze, 1903, no. 80, reprod.; Lapauze, 1911, reprod. p. 453; Zabel, 1930, p. 382, reprod. p. 375; Miller, 1938, pp. 14 and 15; Mongan, 1944, p. 400, reprod. p. 401; Mongan, 1947, no. 23, reprod.; Alazard, 1950, p. 107.

EXHIBITIONS: Paris, 1867, no. 385.

Delphine Bochet, born at Lille in 1785, was the sister of Edme-François-Joseph Bochet and Cécile-Françoise, later Madame Henri-Placide-Joseph Panckoucke. In 1811, while he was working in Rome, Ingres painted the two magnificent portraits of her brother and her sister which are now in the Louvre. Delphine died in Paris in 1876.

Although Madame Ramel was eight years her husband's junior, there is no obvious difference in their ages as they sit at either side of the fireplace, posing for their new son-in-law. Ingres has, incidentally, skillfully minimized the fact that Madame Ramel is somewhat wall-eyed.

*Fogg Art Museum, Harvard University,*
*Bequest of Grenville L. Winthrop, 1943.839*

Graphite on white wove paper. 13⅞ x 10⅝ in. (346 x 268 mm.)

Signed at the lower left: *J. Ingres Del.* | *a son cher cousin* | *et ami Monsieur* | *Gallois —* | *1852*

PROVENANCE: Félix Gallois (Sale, Paris, Georges Petit Gallery, 9-11 June 1914, no. 35, reprod.); Maurice Fenaille; Anonymous sale, Paris, Hôtel Drouot, 23 June 1959, no. 7, pl. IV; Marianne Feilchenfeldt to Robert Lehman, 1960.

EXHIBITIONS: Paris, 1911, no. 169; Nice, Palais des Arts, 1931, *Ingres,* no. 20.

Nathalie Bochet was born in Paris, 22 December 1819. She was the daughter of Edme Bochet and the niece of Madame Panckoucke, whose portraits painted by Ingres in Rome are now in the Louvre. The family "look" was apparently strong among the Bochets, for the shape of Natalie's mouth and the set of her eyes are remarkably like those of her father in his portrait of 1811 (Wildenstein, 1954, pl. 9).

The drawing is dedicated to "his dear cousin, Monsieur Gallois." In the year of this drawing Ingres became a relative of the Gallois through his marriage to Delphine Ramel, the daughter of Nathalie's aunt (No. 104). When he drew Nathalie's likeness, she had already been married to Félix Gallois for twelve years. To date no documents regarding the activities of Monsieur Gallois or his wife have been found in the Paris archives. It seems probable that the couple lived somewhere away from Paris.

*Robert Lehman, New York*

Soft graphite with white chalk highlights on brown wove paper. 14 x 11¼ in. (354 x 285 mm.)

Signed at the lower left: *J Ingres Del | 1852*

Inscribed by the artist in the lower right: *a Son ami | M. Marcotte Genlis*

CONDITION:     The paper has darkened with age and exposure to light. It is lightly foxed throughout; and a stain, approximately ¾ in. wide, extends around the outer edges of the drawing, apparently caused by a previous mounting. There are damaged areas.

PROVENANCE:     Presumably from the sitter to his nephew, Edme-Marie-Antoine Marcotte de Quivières (d. 1881); to his son, Charles Marcotte de Quivières (d. 1913); to his son Bernard Marcotte de Quivières; Marianne Feilchenfeldt, Zurich.

REPRODUCTIONS: Engraved by Luigi Calamatta, 1853.

BIBLIOGRAPHY:     Delaborde, 1870, no. 365, p. 306; Blanc, 1870, p. 246; Lapauze, 1901, p. 267; Hans Naef, "Ingres' Portraits of the Marcotte Family," *The Art Bulletin,* XL, December, 1958, pp. 336-45, reprod. pl. 8.

EXHIBITIONS:     Paris, Palais des Beaux-Arts, 1913, *David et ses élèves,* no. 349.

Marie-Jean-Baptiste-Joseph Marcotte Genlis was born at Doullens in 1781. He was a *Receveur général de finance,* the younger brother of Ingres' closest and oldest friend Marcotte d'Argenteuil (see the *Portrait of Monsieur Marcotte,* 1810, National Gallery, Washington). He was interested in art, particularly the sculpture of Simart (see under No. 110). He visited Ingres in Rome when Ingres was Director of the Villa Medici and Simart a pupil there. M. Marcotte Genlis died in Mézières (Ardennes), 29 April 1867, three and a half months after his old friend. His life span was therefore almost the exact equivalent of the artist's. He was the only one among the eight Marcotte children who never married.

The portrait is to be compared with the one Ingres drew of M. Marcotte Genlis twenty-two years earlier, in 1830 (still in the family, Naef, *op. cit.,* fig. 7).

*Mr. and Mrs. Eugene Victor Thaw, New York*

NUDE STUDY FOR THE FIGURE OF FRANCE IN THE "APOTHEOSIS OF NAPOLEON"

Graphite on white wove paper, squared for enlargement. 17¾ x 6⅜ in. (450 x 162 mm.)

Turquoise stamp of the Ingres Sale at the lower right (L. 1477).

PROVENANCE:   Ingres' atelier; Charles E. Slatkin Galleries, New York, to Nathan J. Cohn.

The *Apotheosis of Napoleon* was commissioned by the government in March, 1853, to decorate the ceiling of the Salon of Napoleon in the Hôtel de Ville. The order stipulated that the painting was to be finished within a year, a stipulation that Ingres met. The painting was destroyed by fire on 24 May 1871, but its appearance is known through a finished oil sketch of the whole composition in the Louvre (Giraudon, 13179), another in the Museum of the City of Paris (Wildenstein, no. 271), and a finished watercolor drawing in the Louvre (no. 5030).

Although Ingres worked with unusual speed to meet the time requirement, he did not vary his habit of giving intense study not only to the whole design, but also to every detail. The rondel decoration was conceived as a large medallion or cameo. As usual, the artist turned to antique sources for the shapes and designs to be used, to ancient coins, cameos and vases.

The naked emperor, standing in a golden chariot drawn by four white horses led by Victory, mounts the heavens from St. Helena. Fame holds a wreath above Napoleon's head. From behind the empty throne an angry Nemesis pursues Crime and Anarchy. France, draped in mourning, watches Napoleon's triumphant rise into the empyrian.

Ingres studied the pose of this figure in this drawing of the nude. The squaring corresponds exactly to the squaring of the draped figure (No. 103), although the scale of the latter is somewhat larger. A comparison of the two offers a dramatic example of the procedure the artist followed, as Raphael, his god, had done in an earlier century.

*Estate of Nathan J. Cohn, Spring Valley, New York*

Soft graphite and black chalk over stylus outlines on tan wove paper, affixed to heavy cream-colored paper and squared for transfer. 20⅝ x 10¾ in. (525 x 274 mm.)

Signed in graphite at the lower left: *Ingres.*

Inscribed at the left: *hortense de fontana | 26 rue St. George 113 | belle tete de | caractere*

Red stamp of the E. Haro Collection at the lower left (L. 1241).

CONDITION:     The upper left corner has been replaced by an inlay of brown wove paper. Two small holes at the upper right, undoubtedly produced when the drawing was removed from a former mount, are still visible. The paper has darkened with age and exposure to light.

PROVENANCE:     In October, 1866, sold by Ingres to E. Haro; Grenville L. Winthrop.

BIBLIOGRAPHY:     Agnes Mongan, *Drawings from the Collection of Curtis O. Baer,* Cambridge, Fogg Art Museum, 1958, p. 54, cited under no. 43.

Ingres himself has made a note at the lower left recording the name and address of the model who posed for him. The pose of the figure itself, except for the arms, and the general disposition of the drapery seem to derive from a relief of a Maenad in the Villa Torlonia Albani.

His studies for the painting (there are more than eighty at Montauban) include everything from quick pen sketches for the general composition to finished studies of individual details. Ingres called upon his pupils for assistance not only in the painting itself, but as models. In addition to "la belle Hortense," the Balze brothers, Raymond and Paul, who assisted him, also posed (Lapauze, 1911, p. 467). In fact, Ingres himself, unlikely as it seems, is said to have sat before Raymond Balze for the figure of Nemesis!

The *Apotheosis* was painted in Gatteaux' studio in the rue de Lille, not in the Louvre studio which Niewerkerke had offered. In February, 1854, when the picture was completed, it was there that Ingres received Emperor Napoleon III and his Empress, the ministers, functionaries, even the curious who came to see the work and to congratulate the seventy-four-year-old artist (Lapauze, 1911, pp. 468-72). The painting was a triumphant success.

*Fogg Art Museum, Harvard University,*
*Bequest of Grenville L. Winthrop, 1943.856*

Graphite on thin white wove paper which has been affixed to a secondary support. $13\frac{15}{16}$ x 10½ in. (353 x 267 mm.)

Signed at the upper left: *(J I)ngres Del*

Inscribed at the upper right: *Madame Delp. Ingres 1855.* When the drawing was mounted in a mat which covered not only a tear at the upper left, but also the artist's signature and inscription, the latter were copied below. At this time the date was inaccurately transcribed *1844.*

CONDITION:     At some time after it had been completed, the drawing was wrapped around a stretcher. Later when it was removed from this mount, it was cut on both sides and at the top to eliminate the stretcher marks. At the bottom where part of the design itself had been damaged, however, the drawing was mended and retouched. The paper has darkened slightly with age and has been lightly stained along the edges by a former wood-pulp mat. The artist has changed the design of the bonnet, both near the right hand and above the left shoulder. Although erased, the earlier drawing is visible.

PROVENANCE:     Riant; Wildenstein to Charles Dunlap, 1948.

There has been, until now, no mention of this portrait in the Ingres literature. It was drawn in the same year that Ingres also made portraits of Delphine's brother Edme and his wife (No. 105) and her sister Mathilde, Madame Norbert Hache (lost during the war).

A painted portrait of Delphine in a similar pose, dated 1859, is in the Oskar Reinhart Collection, Winterthur, Switzerland, but the painting shows only the head and right forearm. The Riants, who once owned the drawing, were relatives of the Ramels.

The drawing is to be published by Phyllis Hattis in an article which will appear in the next number of the *Bulletin du Musée Ingres.*

*Fogg Art Museum, Harvard University,*
*Gift of Charles Dunlap, 1954.110*

y. Ingres Del.

Madame Delp. Ingres 1844.

Graphite accented with white chalk (Mme. Ramel's scarf) on white wove paper. 13½ x 10⅝ in. (342 x 270 mm.)

Signed at the lower center: *à mon cher frere Edmond Ramel | souvenir de Cannes. J. Ingres | 1855.* Inscribed at the upper right: *Portraits de M^r et M^e ed. Ramel*

PROVENANCE:    Edme Ramel (d. 1875); Madame Edme Ramel, née Irma Donbernard (d. 1898); Henri Haro (Sale, Paris, 3 February 1912, no. 141, reprod.); Henry Lapauze (Sale, Paris, Hôtel Drouot, 21 June 1929, no. 34, reprod.); Paul Rosenberg to Benjamin Sonnenberg, 1958.

BIBLIOGRAPHY:    Lapauze, 1903, p. 68, no. 78; Lapauze, 1911, p. 476; Lapauze, *Briant,* 1911, p. 48; *Kunst und Kunstler,* XXVII, July, 1929, reprod. p. 408.

Edme-Marie-Dominique Ramel (as he is called in his official death certificate) was born in Le Puy ca. 1817, nearly a decade after his sister Delphine (No. 104). A customs collector in Cannes, he married Jeanne-Faustine-Marie-Irma Donbernard, born ca. 1821 in Vieille, Aure (Haute-Pyrenées). In September, 1855, when Ingres and his wife visited the Ramels at Cannes, the artist drew this extremely sympathetic portrait. The view of L'Esterel behind the couple is the only landscape background drawn outdoors by Ingres after his departure from Florence.

*Mr. and Mrs. Benjamin Sonnenberg, New York*

à mon cher frère Edmond Ramel
Souvenir de Cannes. J. Ingres 1855

Graphite, pen and brown ink, watercolor (vermilion, lapis blue, turquoise blue, yellow, gray) and white gouache on tracing paper, affixed to white wove paper. 10⅜ x 7⅜ in. (264 x 187 mm.)*

Inscribed in graphite in the lower border: At the left: *S$^t$ ANTOINE Di PAD.* In the center: *J Ingres. fec. | 1855 | à Madame Ingres.* At the right: *S$^t$ LEOPOLDUS.*

CONDITION: The tiny lines that appear to be in the paper are actually the result of irregularities in the affixing of the tracing paper to its support. Since no corresponding irregularities are visible in the design, we can conclude that the tracing paper was glued down before the watercolor was executed. Only slight damage has occurred, two abraded areas on the altar dais between the saints and several tears along the upper edge.

PROVENANCE: Mme. Ingres (Sale, Paris, Hôtel Drouot, 10 April 1894, no. 97); M. Max (Sale, Paris, Georges Petit Gallery, 17 May 1917, no. 64, reprod.); acquired by Grenville L. Winthrop, 1927.

BIBLIOGRAPHY: Delaborde, 1870, p. 267, no. 166; Blanc, 1870, p. 241; *Gazette des Beaux-Arts,* xv, 1877, reprod. in color opp. p. 323; Schlenoff, 1956, pl. xxxix.

The Madonna's pose recalls the composition of the *Vow of Louis XIII,* but the position of the Child is different. Here his arm points down to St. Anthony, and his left knee touches the Madonna's forearm. The choice of saints is an unusual one. St. Anthony of Padua is, of course, well-known and greatly loved, but St. Leopold, an Austrian saint (1080-1136), the patron of Carinthia, rarely appears outside Austria. Ingres has dressed him as a Roman legionnaire, but the spear and the shield are his familiar symbols. On an altar, visible between the two saints, is a chalice with the Host.

The watercolor seems to have been a gift of the artist to his wife and undoubtedly had a personal religious significance. St. Anthony's feast is celebrated on 13 June, St. Leopold's on 15 November.

*Fogg Art Museum, Harvard University,*
*Bequest of Grenville L. Winthrop, 1943.375*

ST ANTOINE DE PAD.     J Ingres. fec.     St LEOPOLDUS

1855.

à Madame Ingres.

Two tones of soft graphite on white wove paper that has faded to ivory; a single white chalk highlight on the arm of the chair. 13⅛ x 9⅞ in. (332 x 251 mm.)

Signed at the lower right: *Son ami et | condisciple Del.ᵛⁱᵗ | J. Ingres | 1856.* Inscribed by the artist at the upper right: *M. J. DELECLUSE*

CONDITION:    The thin paper was stretched around a support (wood or cardboard) before the drawing was executed, and when it was later removed from this mount the edges were seriously torn. The paper has discolored as a result of exposure to light.

PROVENANCE:    The sitter (d. 1863) to his nephew Adolphe Viollet-Le-Duc (d. 1878); his widow (d. 1896) to her son-in-law Alfred Vaudoyer (d. 1917); his son Georges Vaudoyer to Grenville L. Winthrop.

BIBLIOGRAPHY:    E. Saglio, "Un nouveau tableau de M. Ingres, Liste complète de ses oeuvres," *Le Correspondence littéraire,* 5 February 1857, p. 79; Charles Blanc, "Le Salon des Arts-Unis," *Gazette des Beaux-Arts,* I, February 1861, p. 191; Henri Delaborde, "Les dessins de M. Ingres au Salon des Arts-Unis," *Gazette des Beaux-Arts,* IX, 1 March 1861, p. 267; Galichon, 1861, p. 357; Delaborde, 1870, no. 280; Jouin, 1888, p. 49; *Le livre du centennaire du Journal des Débats,* Paris, 1889, reprod. opp. p. 472; Henri Bouchot, "Exposition des portraits des écrivains et journalistes du siècle," *Gazette des Beaux-Arts,* 1 September 1893, pp. 208, 210, 1 October 1893, reprod. opp. p. 312; Duplessis, 1896, no. 7, reprod. photogravure by Charreyre; Lapauze, 1901, pp. 250 (ref. to Cahier X, folio 26), 265; Robert Baschet, *E.-J. Delécluze, témoin de son temps,* Paris, 1942, pp. 61, 414, 439, reprod. opp. p. 41; Mongan, 1944, pp. 401 f., reprod.; Alazard, 1950, p. 107, pl. XCIX; Schlenoff, 1956, p. 295, fn. 2; p. 301, fn. 4; pl. V.

EXHIBITIONS:    Paris, 1861, no. 49; Paris, Georges Petit Gallery, 1893, *Portraits des écrivains et journalistes du siècle,* no 256; Paris, 1911, no. 176; Paris, 1921, no. 126; Paris, Hôtel Charpentier, 1929, *Cent ans de vie française,* no. 288; Paris, 1934, no. 43.

Étienne-Jean Delécluze was born in Paris in 1781, the son of a talented architect. His early studies were interrupted by the Revolution, but a curé near his family's refuge in Meudun found in him a ready and intelligent pupil. Upon his return to Paris, he entered David's studio where he first met Ingres, one year his senior. The two formed a friendship that lasted as long as they lived.

Although Delécluze won a first Medal in 1800 for an *Andromaque,* he recognized that his was not an outstanding pictorial gift, and he turned to writing both art criticism and biography. In the early decades of the century, Delécluze wrote for the *Moniteur.* Then for forty years he was employed by the Bertin brothers (see under No. 68) to write art and music criticism for the *Journal des Débats.* His books included biographies of Petrarch, Roger Bacon, Aeneas Piccolomini, Rabelais and Palestrina. He translated Dante into French and contributed to *Le Plutarque français.* In fact, it was probably Delécluze who persuaded Ingres to make five drawings for that publication in 1844 (see under No. 92). He praised highly the paintings which Ingres showed in the *Exposition Universelle* of 1855. That same year, one year before he sat for this drawing, Delécluze published two books, *Louis David, son école et son temps* and a series of essays, *Les Beaux-Arts.* Ingres has put them on the table near the sitter's elbow.

The lifelong and profound affection of Ingres for his friend is evident not only in the inscription, but also in every line of this thoughtful, reflective and moving portrait. In the forties, Delécluze had been one of a brilliant group which included Prosper Merimée, Stendhal, Ampère and others. His written descriptions of these personages were said by a contemporary to be so frank and true that it was impossible not to believe them perfect likenesses. The same can be said of Ingres' drawing. The grave, measured, kind yet discerning critic who wrote without pedantry and who without stint dedicated himself to his labors until the evening of his death in 1863, had a temperament and stood for values that appealed deeply to the painter.

*Fogg Art Museum, Harvard University,
Bequest of Grenville L. Winthrop, 1943.849*

M<sup>R</sup> J. DELECLUSE.

Son ami et
Condisciple Del<sup>n</sup>
J. Ingres
1856.

LOUIS
DAVID
BEAUX
ARTS

Soft graphite and white chalk on very thin, cream-colored wove paper. 13 x 9⁹⁄₁₆ in. (330 x 243 mm.)

Signed at the lower right: *hommage du | plus affèctueux | dèvouement | Ingres — | 1856*

CONDITION:    Severe foxing and a general darkening of the paper have been minimized by bleaching. A narrow vertical scrape extending from the forehead through the sitter's left eye to the jaw line has been retouched. An old adherent, possibly glue, has stained the upper edge.

PROVENANCE:    Emilien de Nieuwerkerke (d. 1892); presumably to his sole heir, Contessa Altieri, née Cantacuzène; Count Contini to Jacques Seligman and Co., June, 1928; acquired from the latter by Grenville L. Winthrop, November, 1928.

REPRODUCTIONS: Lithographed by Adolphe-Pierre Riffaut, 1856; engraved by C.-M.-F. Dien, 1857.

BIBLIOGRAPHY:    *L'Artiste*, XVII, 3 August 1856, p. 70, reprod., lithograph by Riffaut; Edmond Saglio, "Un nouveau tableau de M. Ingres, Liste complète de ses oeuvres," *La Correspondance littéraire*, 5 February 1857, p. 79; Théophile Gautier, "Les soirées du Louvre," *L'Artiste*, 31 January 1858, pp. 69 ff.; Galichon, 1861, p. 47; Oliver Merson and Emile Bellier de la Chavignerie, *Ingres*, Paris, 1867, p. 120; Delaborde, 1870, no. 384; Blanc, 1870, p. 239; Philippe de Chennevières, "Souvenirs d'un directeur des Beaux-Arts," *L'Artiste*, I, April, 1885, p. 252; Frédéric Henriet, "Le Comte de Nieuwerkerke," *Le Journal des Arts*, 21 January 1893, p. 1; 25 January 1893, p. 2, fn. 1; Frédéric Henriet, "Le Comte E. de Nieuwerkerke," *L'Art*, LVIII, September, 1894, pp. 227, 235, 237, reprod. (detail); Lapauze, 1901, pp. 250 (ref. to Cahier X, folio 26), 267; Lapauze, 1911, reprod. after the engraving by Dien; Mongan, 1944, p. 401; Edmond and Jules de Goncourt, *Journal*, Monaco, 1956, V, entry for 3 January 1863.

EXHIBITIONS:    Paris, 1861; Paris, 1867, no. 381.

Le Comte de Nieuwerkerke was born in Paris in 1811 of a noble Dutch family, many of whom were illustrious soldiers. Rather than a military career, he chose to become a sculptor. He exhibited in the Salons of 1843, 1846 and 1847. Portrait busts of Descartes, Napoleon III, and others won him standing as a sculptor. It was as a functionary, however, that he achieved fame. He was a great friend of Prince Napoleon and Princess Mathilde. In 1848 he was made a Chevalier of the Legion of Honor, in 1855 a Commander and in 1863 Grand Officer. He was made the Director General of the National Museums in 1849 and Superintendent of Fine Arts in 1863.

A supporter of the classical art of the period, he was an antagonist of change. He detested the Barbizon painters and obstructed the progress of the Impressionists; but in his management of the Louvre, he was effective. Villot and Reiset were appointed in his regime.

In strong contrast to the warmth of the previous drawing, here Ingres has given us the pompous, complacent and condescending court official, conscious of his high office and his power. Relations between the two men were often strained. The coolness can be surmised in the tone of the dedication, with its official flavor. Frédéric Henriet, in delivering Nieuwerkerke's eulogy at the Institute in 1894, cited several portraits of the Count but praised the Ingres drawing above all other representations. In Henriet's words: "Nieuwerkerke était au Louvre plus qu'un roi, presque un dieu, et quand il apparaissait le matin dans la galérie, on en dit Jupiter descendant de l'Olympe pour répandre sur les mortels les faveurs et les sourires." His commanding presence—he stood well over six feet tall and was always handsomely dressed—contributed to the effect.

Théophile Gautier in describing Nieuwerkerke's sumptuous apartment in the Louvre noted that this Ingres drawing stood on a table by his bed, counterbalanced on the other side by Ingres' drawing of *Philémon and Baucis*. It had been Nieuwerkerke's intention to bequeath his collection to the Louvre. The events of 1870 outraged him. He withdrew to Italy. He died in 1892 at Gattajola near Lucca. His collection went into private hands, much of it into the possession of Sir Richard Wallace.

*Fogg Art Museum, Harvard University,*
*Bequest of Grenville L. Winthrop, 1943.855*

hommage du
plus affectueux
dévouement
Ingres
1856.

PORTRAIT OF MLLE. CÉCILE-MARIE PANCKOUCKE, LATER MME. TOURNOUËR

Soft graphite on white wove paper. 13¼ x 9¾ in. (325 x 246 mm.)

Signed at the lower right: *à M<sup>r</sup> forgeot | son très affectionné | Ingres Del. | 12 7<sup>bre</sup> 1856*. Previous inscriptions, now erased, are almost illegible. At the upper right: *Mademoiselle Cécile Panckoucke*. At the lower right the inscription, now effaced in part, originally read: *Portrait de M<sup>lle</sup> Cécile Panckoucke | offert à M<sup>r</sup> forgeot | par son très affectionné | Ingres Del. | 12 7<sup>bre</sup> 1856*.

CONDITION: The paper is slightly abraded in areas where the artist has revised the design and inscription. It is also somewhat discolored, presumably as a result of age and exposure to light.

PROVENANCE: Louis-Philippe Morande Forgeot, the sitter's stepgrandfather (d. 1864); to the sitter Mme. Jacques-Raoul Tournouër (d. 1903); to her daughter, Mme. Maurice Bastide du Lude (d. 1951); Maurice Bastide du Lude to Marianne Feilchenfeldt, 1956; Jacques Seligman & Co., to the Detroit Institute of Arts, 1964.

BIBLIOGRAPHY: Delaborde, 1870, no. 388, p. 309; Blanc, 1870, p. 240; Lapauze, 1901, p. 250; Hans Naef, "Notes on Ingres Drawings, III," *The Art Quarterly,* Winter, 1958, pp. 414-17, reprod. p. 410; *Gazette des Beaux-Arts,* LXV, Supplement, February, 1965, p. 56, reprod. no. 224; Hans Naef, "L'Ingrisme dans le monde," *Bulletin du Musée Ingres,* July, 1965, p. 21; Frederick Cummings, "Romantic Portraitist: Three Drawings by Ingres," *Bulletin of the Detroit Institute of Arts,* XLIV, 1965, p. 73, reprod.

EXHIBITIONS: Bordeaux, Galérie de la Société des Amis des Arts, 1865, *Société des Amis des Arts de Bordeaux, 14<sup>e</sup> Exposition,* no. 309; Paris, 1867, no. 393; New York, Jacques Seligman & Co., 1960, *Master Drawings,* no. 19.

Cécile was the daughter of the only son of Madame Panckoucke whose portrait is in the Louvre, painted nearly half a century before this drawing was executed. Madame Panckoucke was married twice. Her second husband was Louis-Philippe Morande Forgeot to whom this drawing is dedicated. Her mother was Marie-Joséphine Marcotte de Quivière, a niece of Ingres' great friend Marcotte d'Argenteuil and the daughter of Antoinette-Félicité-Natalie Bochet, the sister of Madame Ramel (see No. 99).

In addition to the present inscription, a close examination of the drawing shows that there was a first line which was later erased. This read, *"Portrait de Mademoiselle Cécile Panckoucke offert."* As the erased inscription refers to her as "Mademoiselle" and the drawing is dated 12 September 1856, it must have been drawn just a few days before she married, in September, 1856, Jacques-Raoul Tournouër. Although educated to be a lawyer, Tournouër did not follow this profession but became a distinguished geologist.

*The Detroit Institute of Arts*

à M. forgeot
son très affectionné
Ingres Del.
12 7bre 1856.

Graphite. 13¼ x 10¼ in. (335 x 260 mm.)

Signed at the lower right: *a son ami Simard* (sic) | *Ingres Del.* | *1857.*

PROVENANCE:    Charles Simart (d. 1857) to the sitter's father, Prosper Baltard (d. 1862); to the sitter's uncle, Victor Baltard (d. 1874); Wildenstein to Albright Art Gallery, 1932.

BIBLIOGRAPHY:    Galichon, 1861, p. 44; Delaborde, 1870, no. 412, p. 312; Blanc, 1870, p. 239; Lapauze, 1901, p. 290 (Cahier x); R. Shoolman and C. E. Slatkin, *The Enjoyment of Art in America*, Philadelphia and New York, 1942, pl. 508, p. 547; Mongan, 1947, no. 24, reprod.; "Check List of Drawings in the Collection of the Gallery," *Gallery Notes*, Buffalo Fine Arts Academy, XVIII, May, 1954, p. 13, reprod.

EXHIBITIONS:    Paris, 1861; Paris, 1867, no. 389; Buffalo, Albright Art Gallery, 1932, *Nineteenth Century French Art,* no. 83; Buffalo, Albright Art Gallery, 1935, *Master Drawings,* no. 96, reprod.; Springfield, etc., 1939-40, no. 27, reprod.; San Francisco, 1947, no. 16; Detroit, The Detroit Institute of Arts, 1950, *French Painting from David to Courbet,* no. 24; Detroit, The Detroit Institute of Arts, 1 June-15 September 1950, *Old Master Drawings from Midwestern Museums,* no. 27; Winnipeg, Winnipeg Art Gallery, 1954, *French Pre-Impressionist Painters of the 19th Century,* no. 15; Rotterdam, Paris, New York, 1958-59, no. 136, pl. 109; New York, 1961, no. 69.

Charles Simart, winner of a *prix de Rome* for sculpture, was a *pensionnaire* at the Villa Medici during Ingres' directorate. A native of Troyes, Simart was the protégée of Philippe-Marie-Nicolas Marcotte, *Receveur générale des finances* in Troyes, the eldest brother of Ingres' close friend Marcotte d'Argenteuil. After the death of his protector in 1836, Simart continued to enjoy the favor of Ingres' circle, for Marcotte Genlis (see No. 101) carried on his brother's assistance to the young sculptor. Ingres himself chose Simart to make the sculptural decorations, four allegorical friezes, ten oval medallions and the freestanding figure of Minerva, which were to supplement and set off the paintings of the different ages of the world at the Château Dampierre. Simart's career was successful. Among his commissions, for example, were the victories for Napoleon's tomb at the Invalides.

He married Laure Jay, a niece of his friend the architect Victor Baltard who was his contemporary, friend and "condisciple" as a *prix de Rome.* She died in 1851, leaving a small son. A year later, he married his first wife's cousin, Amelie Baltard, the daughter of Prosper Baltard, Victor's brother. Only five years later in 1857, the year the portrait was drawn, Charles Simart died at the age of fifty-one as a result of an accident. Dr. Naef has suggested that Ingres may have drawn this portrait of Mme. Simart to cheer her ill husband.

*Albright-Knox Art Gallery, Buffalo, New York,*
*Elisabeth H. Gates Fund*

à son ami Simard
Ingres Del
1857

Graphite heightened with white chalk.  12⅜ x 9⅝ in.  (320 x 245 mm.)

Signed at the lower right: *Ingres Del │ a Madame │ Louise Marcotte │ 1858 │ 18 octobre.*

PROVENANCE:    Mme. Charles Marcotte d'Argenteuil, née Louise Becquet de Layens, the sitter's mother-in-law to whom the portrait is dedicated (d. 1862); her husband (d. 1864); Mme. Hubert Rohault de Fleury, née Louise Marcotte, the sitter's wife (d. 1873); the sitter (d. 1910); Mme. Jacquin de Margerie, née Charlotte-Louise-Marie Rohault de Fleury, the sitter's daughter (d. 1948); Edouard Bonnefous, Paris; French, New York, to Nathan J. Cohn, 1954.

BIBLIOGRAPHY:    Galichon, 1861, p. 46; Delaborde, 1870, no. 296; Blanc, 1870, p. 236; Hans Naef, "Ingres Portrait Drawings of the Marcotte Family," *Art Bulletin*, XL, December, 1958, pp. 336-45, fig. 20.

EXHIBITIONS:    Paris, 1861; Paris, 1867, no. 335; Paris, 1934, no. 44; Paris, André Weil Gallery, 1949, *Ingres*, no. 50 bis; Paris, Bernheim-Jeune Gallery, 1952, *Cent-cinquante ans de dessins, 1800-1950*, no. 88; New York, 1961, no. 70, reprod.

Hubert Rohault de Fleury, who was born in Paris, 28 December 1826, was the son and brother of noted architects, whose publications on medieval monuments are still familiar to architectural historians. He himself tried various callings, the navy, industry, painting, writing. In 1857 he married Louise-Marie-Chantal Marcotte, the younger daughter of Ingres' great friend, M. Marcotte d'Argenteuil (see Ingres' *Portrait of M. Marcotte,* National Gallery, Washington), and thus came into the Ingres circle. This drawing was made one year after his marriage, according to an old label on the reverse, at the home of M. Marcotte.

Rohault de Fleury became deeply involved in the project of his brother-in-law Legentil, the construction of the church of Sacre Coeur in fulfillment of a national vow. As the project's historian, he later published several volumes which record the full story. Since he lived until 1910, he saw the great structure rise on the summit of Montmartre.

The portfolio under his arm is certainly an allusion to his artistic activities. With his blond hair and pale, clear eyes, he is a striking example of the survival of that type of Frenchman known as a "Gaulois."

*The Estate of Nathan J. Cohn, Spring Valley, New York*

Yngres del
à Madame
Louise Marcotte.
18 octobre 1858.

Graphite on white wove paper. 10⅛ x 8 in. (256 x 202 mm.)

Signed at the lower left: *à | son cher ami Gounod | Ingres Del^{vit} | 1859.*

Inscribed at the upper right: *Portrait de M^e. Ch.^{les} Gounod.*

CONDITION:     The paper is slightly discolored and scattered with minor chives.

PROVENANCE:    Charles Gounod (d. 1893); the sitter, Mme. Charles Gounod (d. 1906); their daughter
               Jeanne, La Baronne Pierre de Lassus Saint-Geniès, to Paul Brame, Paris, 1942; César de
               Hauke to Mrs. Chauncey McCormick.

BIBLIOGRAPHY:  Delaborde, 1870, no. 310; Lapauze, 1903, no. 28, reprod.; Hans Naef, "Portrait Drawings
               by Ingres in the Art Institute of Chicago," *Museum Studies,* I, Winter, 1966, pp. 66-83,
               reprod.

EXHIBITIONS:   Paris, Grand Palais, 1900, *Exposition centennale de l'art français,* no. 1090; Paris, Palais
               du Domaine de Bagatelle, 1908, *Portraits d'hommes et de femmes célèbres,* no. 106, re-
               prod.; Rotterdam, Paris, New York, 1958-59, no. 137, pl. 106.

Anna Zimmerman, born in Paris, 31 May 1820, was one of the four charming daughters of the well-
known composer, Pierre Zimmerman, a noted professor at the Paris Conservatory. She married
Charles Gounod in 1852. Ingres drew this portrait in 1859, when Madame Gounod was thirty-nine.
The artist was nearly eighty. It gives visible proof not only of the continuing friendship of Ingres
and Gounod, to whom the drawing is dedicated, but also of the extraordinary control of the vener-
able artist's hand and the continuing warmth of his understanding.

Madame Gounod gave not only affection and protection to her gifted husband, but the highest
moral support as well. She was in life as Ingres reveals her here, intelligent, modest, discreet, but
also independent and wise.

*The Art Institute of Chicago,*
*Gift of Messrs. Charles Deering McCormick,*
*Brooks McCormick and Roger McCormick, 1964*

Portrait de M.<sup>e</sup> Ch.<sup>ble</sup> Gounod.

à
Son cher ami Gounod
Ingres Del.<sup>t</sup>
1859.

Oil on six pieces of canvas which have been set into another canvas. 11⅜ x 14⅛ in. (290 x 359 mm.)

PROVENANCE:    Anonymous sale, Paris, 29 November 1886, lot 46; Baron Mourre (Sale, Paris, 28 March 1892, lot 26); Jacques Mathey; E. and A. Silberman Galleries, Inc.

BIBLIOGRAPHY:  Wildenstein, 1954, no. 306, p. 230, fig. 192; *Art Quarterly,* XVII, Winter, 1954, reprod. p. 414.

EXHIBITIONS:   Notre Dame, Indiana, University of Notre Dame, 1959, *The Great Century, France, 1800-1900* (catalogue without numbers).

For the painting *Jesus Among the Doctors* Ingres made nearly one hundred preparatory studies, including drawings and oil sketches. The Indianapolis sketch actually consists of individual small studies on canvas which have been set into another canvas to form a group. It was not unusual for Ingres to make numerous oil sketches in working out a composition, but it is exceptional to have one in an American museum. Ingres bequeathed the majority of them to Montauban.

King Louis Philippe commissioned the painting in 1842 at the request of Queen Marie-Amélie who intended to install it in the chapel of the Château de Bizy. Although Ingres began to make preliminary studies in the forties, work on the painting was suspended and not resumed for twenty years. By this time Ingres had obtained the right to dispose of it. He nevertheless returned to the picture and finished it in 1862, five years before his death, at which time it still remained in his studio. His will directed that the painting and the preparatory studies be given to Montauban where they are today in the collection of the Musée Ingres.

A preliminary drawing for a figure at the left of the composition, an outline drawing of a female nude, squared for enlargement, is on the reverse of the *Study for Mme. Moitessier* (No. 97).

*Art Association of Indianapolis,*
*Herron Museum of Art*

Watercolor (gray, crimson, orange, yellow, brown, purple, pale green) over graphite, heightened with white gouache and accented with black oil paint on heavy white wove paper which had been lightly squared in graphite. 13½ x 9 in. (232 x 228 mm.)

CONDITION:     Scattered foxing on the couch has been minimized by spot bleaching. A tiny hole in the pillow to the right of the bather's elbow has been patched, and a scrape ¼ inch high at the lower left has been stained in brown. Pricks along the left and bottom edges mark off the squaring lines.

PROVENANCE:    Mme. Albert Ramel; acquired by Grenville L. Winthrop in 1929.

BIBLIOGRAPHY:  Mongan, 1944, p. 403.

Ingres signed and dated *The Bather,* known as the *Valpinçon Bather,* Rome 1808. As happened so often, he returned to the subject again and again, frequently with variations. Unlike the watercolor of 1864, now in the Bonnat Museum, Bayonne (*Les dessins de la collection Léon Bonnat au Musée de Bayonne,* III, Paris, 1926, pl. 72), where he has represented a Turkish bath in the background, this version is a nearly exact, if greatly reduced, replica of the famous painting of 1808.

When Mr. Birnbaum wrote to Mr. Winthrop recommending the purchase of the watercolor (June, 1928), he commented that all the drawings which he had seen at the Ramels' were mentioned in Ingres' will, and that this watercolor was described by Ingres as by his own hand. So far, we have not been able to find a copy of the will. If Ingres described the watercolor as by his own hand, it would settle the question, once raised, whether this watercolor might not be by one of the Master's students rather than by Ingres himself. (See also the Technical Appendix.)

*Fogg Art Museum, Harvard University,*
*Bequest of Grenville L. Winthrop, 1943.377*

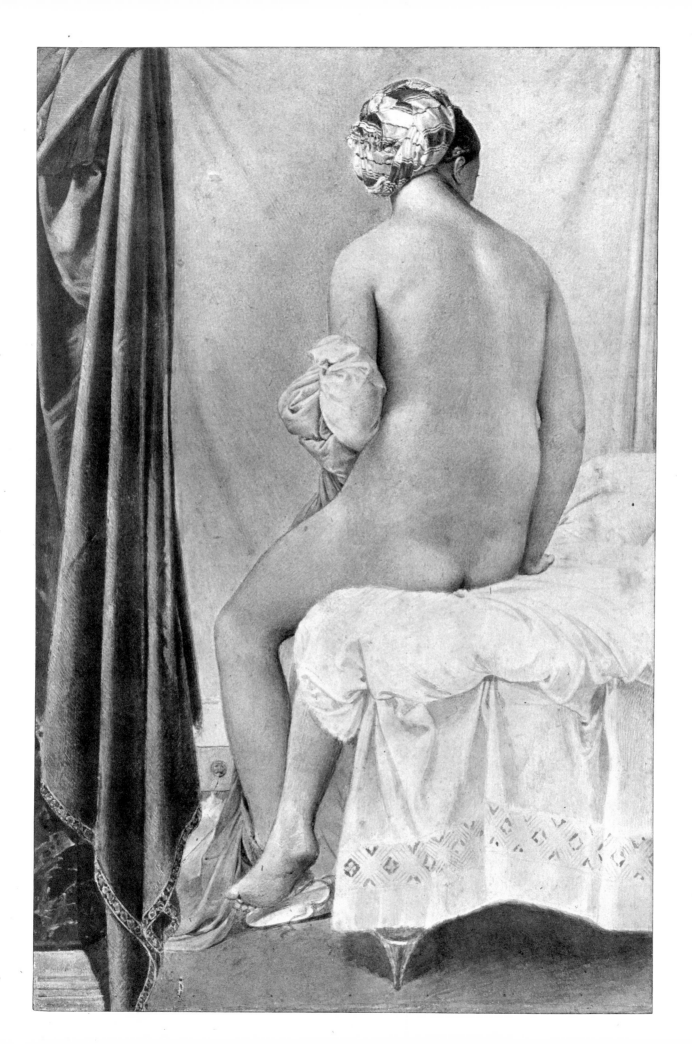

Graphite, watercolor (vermilion, crimson, blue, yellow, gray, violet, pale green and brown), and white gouache on tracing paper, affixed to heavy white wove paper and irregularly varnished. Entire sheet: 7⅛ x 6⅝ in. (199 x 160 mm.) Design area: 4¼ x 5⅛ in. (185 x 148 mm.)*

Signed in the lower border at the left: *J. Ingres P.IT*; at center: *LE CARDINAL DA BIBIENA FIANCE SA NIECE A RAPHAEL 1864.*

CONDITION:     The tracing paper was affixed to the support before the watercolor was applied.

PROVENANCE:     Louis Kronberg; Martin Birnbaum to Grenville L. Winthrop, May, 1928.

BIBLIOGRAPHY:     Schlenoff, 1956, pl. XVIII, opp. p. 145.

During his early years in Rome, Ingres planned a series of paintings illustrating various incidents in the life of Raphael. Delaborde lists eight episodes (pp. 327-28); of that group only the *Fornarina* (Fogg Art Museum) was ever completed. Surviving drawings show Ingres' plans for some of the other subjects. The theme of Raphael's betrothal, not included in the list of eight, was a subject commissioned in 1812 by Caroline Murat, Queen of Naples (Delaborde, 1870, p. 280).

In his notes (Cahier VII and IX), Ingres recorded his preparatory reading about Raphael's life: Vasari, Baglione, Passeri, Baldinucci and Comolli (Schlenoff, 1956, pp. 137 and 138). Bernardo Dovizi da Bibbiena, a boyhood friend of Raphael's in Urbino, raised to the Cardinalate by Leo X, offered his niece in marriage to the painter. Unfortunately, she was of a frail constitution and died before the wedding took place.

A finished drawing of the scene, signed and dated 1812, entered the Louvre with the Hauguet-Coutan Bequest (5029). In that drawing, the Cardinal, whose likeness is taken from Raphael's portrait of Bibbiena (Pitti) stands before a doorway. Through this opening one sees, at the right, the same view that Ingres used a year later in the background of the Fogg's *Fornarina*. In the painting of the *Betrothal*, now in the Walters Gallery, Baltimore, the doorway is draped by a light curtain, drawn aside by a page. In the painting the young woman crosses one hand above the other, against her body, in a gesture of modesty or reluctance. In the 1864 Fogg repetition the artist has returned to the gesture of the 1812 drawing, and has kept the figure of the page who appears in the background of the painting. The illustration in Magimel's book of 1851 (no. 30) is nearer to the Fogg drawing than the Louvre version. It includes the page, but not the chair behind the Cardinal.

*Fogg Art Museum, Harvard University,*
*Bequest of Grenville L. Winthrop, 1943.374*

CARD. BIBIANVS

J. Jacques P.T.          LE CARDINAL DA BIBIENA FIANCE SA NIECE A RAPHAEL          1864.

Watercolor (vermilion, blue, tan and violet) and white gouache over graphite on tracing paper, which has been affixed to heavy cream-colored paper and varnished. 11⅞ x 16¾ in. (301 x 425 mm.)

Signed at the lower left: *J. Ingres E.ⁱᵗ sur un trait de Vase Grec. 1863.* (The inscription referring to the Nereids at the upper left has been effaced.) Inscribed at the center: *ENLEVEMENT D'EUROPE Pline parle d'un tableau d'Antyphile qui represente Europe | Peut etre cette composition est elle une imitation de cet ouvrage celebre | ou une autre de Pythagoras Peintre et Sculpteur.* Inscribed at the lower right: *NEPTUNE couronné d'une feuille de pin | il ordonne à la mer d'etre Calme.*

CONDITION:     Ingres retouched certain areas of the design. For example, in the group of Nereids at the upper left, the white gouache in which they are drawn is over the varnish. The paper has discolored as a result of age and exposure to light, thus modifying the original effect of the watercolors.

PROVENANCE:   In October, 1866, sold by Ingres to E. Haro (Sale, Paris, Hôtel Drouot, 27 April 1867, no. 15); Victor Baltard (the designer of Ingres' funeral monument in Père Lachaise Cemetery); Arnould family, Rheims; P. Arnould, Paris; Arthur B. Davies; Stephen C. Clark, New York; Édouard Jonas to Grenville L. Winthrop, April, 1930.

BIBLIOGRAPHY: Charles Lenormant and Baron J. de Witte, *Élite des monuments céramographiques,* Paris, 1844, I, pl. xxvII, model for composition; Delaborde, 1870, p. 268, no. 173; Royal Cortissoz, *The Painter's Craft,* New York, 1930, pp. 193-98; Mongan, 1944, pp. 411-12, fig. 21; Schlenoff, 1956, pl. xxxv, opp. p. 256.

The central scene is derived from a reproduction of a Greek vase published by Charles Lenormant (*op. cit.*). Ingres probably did not have an opportunity to study the vase, which entered the collection of the British Museum in 1846 (H. B. Walters, *Catalogue of Vases in the British Museum,* London, 1896, IV, p. 95, no. 7184a); but he owned a copy of the Lenormant volume, now preserved in the Musée Ingres, Montauban. This fact explains, at least in part, his misunderstanding of certain details which do not read clearly in the reproduction. The latter does not record the damage which the vase itself has suffered in the course of time. For example, the strange shape between the bull's front legs is the tail of a dolphin now reconstructed on the vase but left incomplete by Lenormant. The group of Galatea with the Nereids, added at the upper left by Ingres after the composition had been finished, probably is also a direct copy from antiquity. Several Graeco-Roman and Roman engraved gems are very close in composition and movement.

Although the drawing is dated two years before the artist's death and although this is a unique version, the watercolor was probably long in gestation. On close examination it can be seen that not only has the first inscription been erased and another (also in Ingres' own hand) been substituted, but also the figure of Poseidon reveals several changes in contour. Ingres has gone back to the texts of antiquity for his colors, following Ovid who described Europa as wearing a white dress and red cloak.

It is not without interest that this is the only watercolor on the list of drawings sold to Haro by Ingres three months before his death. It is equally worth recording that a note on the back once stated that the drawing had belonged to Arthur B. Davies (Cortissoz, *op. cit.*) a note that was no longer on the drawing when it reached the Fogg Museum.

*Fogg Art Museum, Harvard University,*
*Bequest of Grenville L. Winthrop, 1943.378*

ENLEVEMENT D'EUROPE.

NEPTUNE. Couronné. Nuage. Coquille de
l'oreille. Sa mère D'après Columne.

Pline, parle D'un tableau D'Antigonus qui représente Europe.
Peut être celui. Composition et attribute. Neptune. Bas? ouvrage Calcédon.
ou tiré partie De Pythagoras D'allas et Sculpteur.

Ingres. fecit un an sent D'avoir pour Rome. 1805.

Fig. 1. PORTRAIT OF MARIE MARCOTTE (No. 65), Yale University Art Gallery,
Bequest of Edith Malvina K. Wetmore.
Photograph of the entire sheet, including the creases from the drawing's former mount.

# TECHNICAL APPENDIX

FOR THIS CATALOGUE the Fogg Art Museum's Ingres drawings and many of those sent by lenders were unframed, and a technical re-examination of each was undertaken. As expected, new pigments were identified, previously unknown watermarks and stamps were discovered, and in one case a sketch on the verso of a sheet was uncovered. Furthermore, this re-examination offered new, more general insights into Ingres' working methods. Categories of techniques became apparent, each with a definite function in the development of finished compositions. These groups may have been previously well established on the basis of stylistic and historical analyses, yet a further technical understanding does cast new light on Ingres' personal approach to different representational problems. It also aids the twentieth-century student in his mental reconstruction of those fragile sheets now often damaged and disfigured.

The portrait drawings have been of particular interest, standing alone as a distinctive accomplishment, long since recognized as such, but inadequately understood in their technical aspects. More conclusions useful to the Ingres scholar can be safely drawn from them than from the studies for painted works and the occasional sketches. The reader is cautioned, however, that all the following analyses and interpretations have been formed from a relatively small sample, namely, forty-two drawings at the Fogg and three others: the *Portrait of Marie Marcotte* (No. 65) from Yale University, the parchment rondel (No. 3) from the Rosenwald Collection, Jenkintown, Pennsylvania, and the *Portrait of a Lady* (No. 72) from the collection of Mrs. Card, Boston. By a happy chance, these three drawings, placed at our disposal over a period of months, are of the highest individual technical interest and have contributed greatly toward a general understanding of Ingres' methods. Yet other works, unavailable for close and lengthy examination but included in this exhibition, may modify and even contradict the conclusions set forth below. With this caveat before us, we turn first to the portraits.

*Marie Marcotte* holds the key to the portrait drawings' original structure (see fig. 1). Once its construction is understood, our intuitive appreciation of the subtlety of Ingres' touch, of the visual balance between figure and sheet, and of the definition of each personality is made explicit. *Marie Marcotte* came to the Fogg Conservation Department for treatment of a general surface discoloration, which, incidentally, was never undertaken. Upon examination, the author became convinced that the drawing's cardboard mount was not merely contemporary with the portrait, which is dated 1830, but actually antedated it; that is, that Ingres drew on a prepared tablet, purchased from an art supply house, much as an artist today might use prestretched canvas of a standard size. This supposition was based on nothing more than the fact that the pencil lines stopped at the tablet's edge and in no case continued around the folded sheet to the back. It was confirmed by tangible evidence uncovered in the course of restoration.

The drawing sheet was wrapped around ⅛ in. thick cardboard of the poorest quality, glued at the sides, and at the edges folded to the back. These edges had subsequently been overlaid with as many as five layers of paper, paper tapes, and labels. The drawing was in no way adhered to the front of the tablet. It was decided to remove the sheet entire, if possible, by unwrapping it from the back. This was done.

[ 241 ]

Fig. 2. PORTRAIT OF ÉTIENNE GONIN (No. 73), Fogg Art Museum, Harvard University,
Gift of Marian Harris Phinney.
Infrared photograph showing the extensive erasures in the sitter's torso.

In excavating through the layers on the back to reach the edges of the drawing sheet, a previously hidden label was unearthed, that of E.-F. Haro, Ingres' art materials supplier as well as good friend. This label, located just above the sheet's edges, was glued on upside down relative to the drawing on the front and to every other label and inscription on the back. It had certainly been applied before the drawing was begun and the orientation of the tablet established. Further proof of the tablet's manufacture before the portrait's execution was given when the sheet was removed from its mount and flattened. It was then readily observed that the paper had been wrapped around its cardboard slightly askew. Thus the baby sits at a tilt relative to the sheet's edges, which are deckle edges and therefore original and uncut.

Between the drawing and the mount was wrapped a second sheet, not the cream wove paper of the drawing surface, but rather a pale blue, high quality, antique laid sheet. One wonders whether originally, before the drawing sheet darkened, this cool tone carried through to the front. The secondary sheet was undoubtedly included to protect the surface layer against the rough texture and acidic contents of the mount. Viewing the construction as a whole, however, one sees that it had a further use. The entire structure, a taut yet cushioned surface, could not have been improved upon in its lively response to the draughtsman's touch. It must have been a delight to the artist, far superior to a loose sheet or to one entirely adhered to a rigid support, and exactly comparable in its stimulating resilience to a well-stretched canvas. Such a structure also gave the drawing far more presence as a complete and substantial work of art than ever could have been obtained from one on a loose sheet. The format was, therefore, entirely in keeping with the rôle of Ingres' portrait drawings in the eyes of both artist and sitters. (Unfortunately for this argument, in the case of *Marie Marcotte,* the sitter probably had very little immediate appreciation of such subtleties.)

Having recognized the advantages of the tablet structure in this instance, one naturally wonders if it is an exception or Ingres' usual format. I am indebted to Dr. Naef for the information that two drawings, portraits of M. and Mme. Hittorff, still remain on their original tablets in the Louvre. It has also been profitable to examine portraits now existing as loose sheets; for where the paper had been folded around a tablet it acquired a distinctive crease. It is typically rather soft, owing to the cushioning secondary support, very soiled, and with notched, clean corners. Pencil lines stop at the crease. Once recognized, this fold, even when flattened out, can never be mistaken for the all too common stain left by a poor quality, wood pulp mat. Within the Fogg collection, it was found on one or more edges of *M. Jordan and his Daughter* (No. 40), *Mme. Jordan and her Son* (No. 41), *Countess Apponyi* (No. 55), *M. Étienne Gonin* (No. 73), and *M. Delécluze* (No. 107), and perhaps on *M. Guillon Lethière* (No. 19). *M. and Mme. Ramel* (No. 105), *Mme. Gonse* (No. 92), *M. Ruxthiel* (No. 16), and *M. Rohault de Fleury* (No. 111), recently received from private lenders, bear similar indications of their original tablets. From the examination of photographs of other works in the exhibition, it appears that *Dr. Robin* (No. 13), *Mme. Lethière and her Daughter* (No. 31), and *Lady Cavendish-Bentinck* (No. 38) also retain some sign of a tablet crease. As for the portrait drawings having no trace of such folds, one can only suppose that conservators seeking to release them from their corrosive mounts took the quick, less hazardous route and cut them off from the front, leaving the sheets' edges, crease and all, on the boards. Thus one must regretfully assume that many Ingres portrait drawings have been cropped. With the accumulation of more tablet dimensions it may be possible to form a set of standard sizes and from these estimate the amount of loss and the change in figure-to-sheet proportions. So far we have:

| 1 tablet | 450 x 350* | *Countess Apponyi* |
|---|---|---|
| 2 tablets | 440 x 325* | *M. Jordan, Mme. Jordan* |
| 1 tablet | 335* x 265* | *M. and Mme. Ramel* |
| 3 tablets | 325* x 245* | *M. Delécluze, Mme. Gonse, M. Ruxthiel* |
| 1 tablet | 320* x 245* | *M. Rohault de Fleury* |
| 2 tablets | 270* x 215* | *M. Hittorff, Mme. Hittorff* |
| 2 tablets | 245* x 190* | *Marie Marcotte, M. Étienne Gonin* |
| 1 tablet | 245 x 190 | *Mme. Lethière and her Daughter* |
| 1 tablet | 225 x 165 | *M. Guillon Lethière* |
| 1 tablet | 215 x 165 | *Lady Cavendish-Bentinck.* |

The dimensions are in millimeters. Those marked with an asterisk are certain; the others are probable. The certain ones, it should be noted, are all in multiples of five. The dates of these portraits span almost fifty years, from *Dr. Robin* of 1808 to *M. Delécluze* of 1856. Evidently the format suited Ingres throughout his career.

The tablets' drawing surfaces were formed by close-grained, cream, wove sheets. One particular weight of paper stands out as typical. It can be characterized as "Whatman type," for it seems identical to *The Family of Lucien Bonaparte* sheet (No. 33), which is watermarked "J WHATMAN | 1813." The Whatman firm made many kinds of paper, of course, and a lighter weight, wove sheet marked with the Whatman monogram is another less common but equally characteristic type used by Ingres, as in his portraits of the Count and Countess Apponyi (Nos. 56, 55). This paper is so fine that it would seem hardly possible to execute such drawings unless they were strengthened and cushioned by a tablet. Indeed, in *Countess Apponyi,* not only are vestiges of a mounting crease visible at the sides; but also, in darker areas, such as the shading around her hem, the texture of a now lost, antique laid lining sheet is clearly seen.

The various papers used for the portraits are in no way similar to the heavily textured laid paper known today as "Ingres paper." Instead, their closest analogy in weight and surface quality would be parchment. Ingres worked on parchment in two youthful rondel portraits in this exhibition (Nos. 2, 3). For these he used the flesh side of the skin rather than the hair side, contrary to traditional practice. One supposes that the slightly greater amount of "tooth" given to the surface by the preparation used on the flesh side by parchment manufacturers was attractive to him. With the perfection of wove paper by the turn of the century, Ingres had at his disposal a surface more tractable, more regular, and certainly cheaper than parchment. He could thus expand the scale of his portrait drawings, eventually into a work of the magnitude of *The Family of Lucien Bonaparte,* without compromising his preference for a parchment-type surface. This preference was a very individual trait, integral to his entire drawing style. It was not derived from his early models, such as works by Cochin, which were drawn on the more customary laid paper.

The medium of the portrait drawings is graphite pencil. Toward the beginning of his career Ingres favored a sharp, soft pencil, as in the Rosenwald rondel and *Mme. Guillon Lethière* (No. 9). Later his point tended to be duller and greyer, as in *M. Étienne Gonin* and *Mme. Ingres*

(No. 104). It is impossible to establish a rigid sequence, however, as both graphite and touch vary greatly from drawing to drawing. At all times he seems to have kept his pencil, sharp or dull, in a chisel-shaped point, so that he could vary the width of his stroke at will without the delay of changing points. This raises the question: did Ingres ever use more than one pencil in his portrait drawings for a greater variety of line and tone? A few affirmative examples stand out, notably the very finished and elaborate conceptions of *M. Jordan and his Daughter* and *Mme. Jordan and her Son*. Yet with most of the drawings it is a moot point, requiring a more comprehensive examination. Until this is undertaken, one must assume the general use of only one pencil.

There are several very interesting exceptions, however. One such is *Mrs. Vesey and Lady Colthurst* (No. 36). This double portrait, done in the same decade as those of the Jordans, is an equally elegant, highly finished, technical tour de force. The figures have a consistent tone throughout, despite the great variety of shadings. Evidently a single point was used for them. The background indication of an interior seems to be in a greyer graphite than the rest of the drawing, as does the delicately outlined crown of Lady Colthurst's hat, an obvious correction over an erasure. One might guess that the drawing was completed in a single pencil without the architecture and with a larger chapeau. When Ingres (or the sitter) decided that the hat had to be reduced, the general composition was thrown out of balance and so the architecture was added —in another pencil.

A second use of two pencils gives an even more interesting glimpse of Ingres' work in progress. *M. Delécluze* was apparently completed as a relatively informal portrait in a single pencil with a soft, dark tone and left unsigned. At some later time, Ingres presented it to his friend, adding a warm inscription. To augment the air of homage and devotion given by his words, the artist at the same time erased a little heap of books by M. Delécluze's elbow and made a more impressive stack of the sitter's own works, their titles conspicuously displayed as a testimony to their author's knowledge and achievements. This change in the actual concept of the piece is betrayed by the dull, slightly greyer, much harder point used.

Especially in his later portraits, Ingres used white chalk for indications of form and light, as on the arm of M. Delécluze's chair and in the sky behind Count Apponyi, and also of hue, as on Mme. Ramel's handkerchief (No. 99). Often these varying functions are combined in a single drawing, as in *Countess Apponyi*. The chalk has been chemically tested in several cases and found to be calcium carbonate ($CaCO_3$). In two cases, *M. Étienne Gonin* and the *Portrait of a Stocky Young Man* (Fogg accession number 1943.857, not included in this exhibition), it was felt that the white areas had been retouched; and in both cases the pigment was analyzed as white lead ($PbCO_3$). Lack of lead content in a suspect area should never be interpreted as a proof of original pigment, however, as calcium carbonate remains in use to this day.

The best Ingres portrait drawings present an image of incredible technical virtuosity, yet even in those which are apparently the most spontaneous and assured there are usually some erasures. The high quality paper and the rigid support formed a surface durable enough to withstand extensive alterations. Some of these were major changes in the position of a limb, as seen in M. Delécluze's arms; there were also changes in the size and position of accessories, as in Mme. Ingres' side table (No. 104). One constantly recurring type of erasure is outstanding. As is clearly seen in *M. Jordan and his Daughter, Mme. Jordan and her Son, Mme. Hayard and her Daugh-*

*ter* (No. 28), *Mrs. Vesey and Lady Colthurst,* and *Mme. Ingres* (No. 104), Ingres consistently reduced and concentrated the outline of figures. Particularly notable are the erasures around the heads, in coiffures and hats. In the case of M. Jordan, the deletions above his head were so extensive that the paper was virtually worn through. Considering their systematic uniformity of purpose, they seem to have the greatest relevance to an understanding of Ingres' formal preoccupations, showing the evolution of a transcript of reality, with all its accidental effects, into a unified work of art.

The most extensive erasures are seen in the portrait of Étienne Gonin. Ingres eliminated the entire lower half of the sitter's torso, substituting an inscription, and entirely redrew the coat front in order to consolidate the now truncated figure. Some particles of graphite remain imbedded in the erased lines, however, and an infrared photograph reveals the original conception (see fig. 2). M. Gonin, now appearing as a wistful, distant personality, was formerly standing with his coat pulled open and his hands stuffed into his pockets in a very masculine gesture. His facial expression, influenced in our eyes by this stance, did not seem reticent, as now, but cooly appraising, with a touch of amused skepticism. With the changing of the form from a vigorous, broad pyramid to a less substantial, vertical medallion, the sitter himself was transformed and made docile. One wonders whether the artist or Étienne's parents instigated the change; possibly M. and Mme. Jean-Pierre Gonin did not want to think of their son as a grown man of independent character.

Some explanation must be given for the portrait drawings' present condition, for they have deteriorated terribly as a group. Virtually without exception, they were executed on paper of the highest quality, but as we have seen, this was wrapped around a very poor grade cardboard, the acids of which soon began to contaminate the drawing sheet itself. By now, most of the drawings have been transferred onto other mounts. Unfortunately, in the nineteenth century their remounting coincided with the development of the most destructive cardboards and matting materials imaginable, and these dangerous properties were not often immediately recognized. Those drawings on the lightest weight sheets, in particular, have suffered irreparable damage. In all cases deterioration was accelerated by exposure to light. Unlike most drawings, which until this century were usually collected in closed albums, the portraits have always been considered finished, formal works of art. They were constantly exhibited, often by the sitters' descendants, who were certainly well-intentioned, yet understandably ignorant of even the most basic curatorial procedures. When a drawing darkened beyond recognition, radical restorative measures were often undertaken which sometimes further corrupted the paper, destroying its lustrous surface. Many of the portrait drawings are only shadows of their former selves.

The study sheets present a much more varied appearance than the portrait drawings, although here too certain generalizations may be drawn. A cursory inspection reveals a large proportion of actual working drawings, studies which served not merely as inspirations but as exact renderings of composition and detail to be reworked and transferred from sheet to sheet, eventually culminating in an integrated whole. In some cases we have in this exhibition more than one drawing from a given series, as in the four studies related to the painting of *Virgil Reading from the "Aeneid"* (Nos. 20, 21, 22, and 93) and two studies for the oil portrait of Mme. d'Haussonville (Nos. 85 and 86). At times these sheets were drawn after the painted works; yet as in number 93, they usually remain in every sense studies, with extensive reworkings. Even if we have only one representative of a series, its role in a sequence is often betrayed by its technical aspects. For example, the *Hand of M. Bertin* (No. 68) and the *Forestier Family* (No. 5) are on a type of tracing paper known as *papier calque.* Others such as *A Crouching Nude Youth* (No. 60) and *Roger Delivering Angelica* (No. 52), are squared, with the grid often erased and shifted as the artist reconsidered the position of different elements in a composition. Still others, notably the study for *The Golden Age* (No. 87), were transferred from sheet to sheet with a stylus. Only a very few, such as the drapery study for the portrait of *Mme. d'Haussonville* (No. 86), lack technical indications of transfer. Even here, however, tone and line notations indicate that it represents only an incomplete aspect of a larger conception.

At times Ingres transformed a drawing which originally had all the characteristics of a working study into a finished and self-sufficient image. For example, during the execution of the study for *The Golden Age,* he mounted it on a second sheet and probably at that point drew in its framing lines. Yet the drawing is obviously only one of a series; for the sheet is squared, perhaps to facilitate the transfer of its outlines from another page, perhaps to reproduce the completed drawing on another scale. When completed, after many alterations, the figures were heavily traced with a stylus. It was undoubtedly to strengthen the paper against this procedure that Ingres mounted the lightweight sheet onto a more durable support, which also bears the stylus' impress. Although it is not actually *papier calque,* the drawing sheet is so thin that the sketch might originally have been traced from another study, thus introducing the possibility of even a third method of transfer in a single work.

The drapery study for the Madonna in *The Vow of Louis XIII* (No. 54) illustrates the use of a stylus for its transfer from another study, for there are no traces of pigment in the deeply indented lines left by the point. The drawing is executed on the back of an engraving. This seemingly casual choice of paper was not quite as random as might first appear. The sheet is heavy and resilient, as is necessary for a good printed impression of a large plate; consequently it reproduces admirably the line of the stylus.

As in the above case, Ingres' selection of paper always seems to have been a technically knowledgeable, carefully considered decision. It is instructive to note the great variety of sheets used in the working sketches, which served so many different purposes, and to contrast them with the uniformity of paper type we have already observed in his portraits. Not surprisingly, in *Roger Delivering Angelica,* an instance of a preparatory study where the paper is identical to that "Whatman type" seen so often in the portrait drawings, line and tonal indications are very much in the contemporary portraits' style. This work is another example of a working sketch transformed into a finished piece. There are extensive erasures, especially in the hippogriff, which have been assiduously covered with a network of accents in another darker pencil; and some traces of a squaring grid remain visible, although the artist made a careful effort to erase them completely.

Ingres' use of *papier calque* may be subdivided into two categories. One is here represented by various studies of hands (Nos. 74, 75, 68, and 84). We must assume that these drawings, like many of his studies, were originally tracings from other works. Otherwise, he would not have utilized the paper's most notable characteristic, its transparency. *Papier calque* offers a slick surface, not especially appropriate for the charcoal used in the *Hand of the Duc d'Orléans* (No. 84), for example. All the studies of hands are now entirely adhered to a heavily textured laid paper.

Some, including the above drawing, may have been so mounted before their shading was completed; others, including the *Left* and *Right Hand* of Comte Molé (Nos. 74 and 75) were evidently finished over a grainy wove sheet. In all cases, their shadings benefit greatly in transparency and liveliness from the rough supporting papers' texture which comes through the thin intervening layer of *papier calque*. In this curious combination of sheets, Ingres capitalized on the most useful characteristics of each.

The other class of drawings on *papier calque* contains highly finished pencil, ink, and watercolor studies, typified by *Virgil Reading from the "Aeneid"* (No. 93) and *The Madonna and Child with Two Saints* (No. 106). Their complex designs were also probably traced from other working drawings. Yet they must have been applied to their present secondary supports very early in the process of their execution, for otherwise it would have been impossible to work and rework their delicate surfaces without causing the sheets to buckle and wear through. It is initially very difficult to understand why *papier calque* was used except as it might have facilitated a traced under-drawing, for in the case of these watercolors, their backing papers are not heavily textured. Indeed, they are distinguished by their fine surface. Yet with longer study, it seems that together *papier calque* and its slick-surfaced mounting resemble nothing so much as parchment. The rather opaque watercolors and the formal compositions in the classic manner only augment this impression, vaguely suggesting Renaissance book illumination in their luminosity and precision. It appears that Ingres may have had very complex motives in using *papier calque* and that he possessed the technical ingenuity to realize his conceptions.

Other Ingres watercolors, such as the *Dream of Ossian* (No. 17) and *The Bather* (No. 114), which are on more conventional white, opaque paper, are more finished pieces without major reworkings. It is interesting to note in *The Bather,* however, the equivalent in the watercolor technique of Ingres' most consistent pattern of erasures in the portrait drawings, that is, the consolidation of outlines. One cannot satisfactorily erase watercolor; therefore, where the artist wished to simplify and reduce the silhouette of the turban, head, and shoulders, he was forced to paint it out with opaque white rather than rub it away.

Ingres seems to have used colored papers only rarely; and in examples such as studies for *Virgil Reading from the "Aeneid"* (Nos. 21 and 22), the paper's tint has undoubtedly intensified with the sheets' deterioration over the years. These drawings and others, including the drapery study for the figure of Virgil in *The Apotheosis of Homer* (No. 58), are largely concerned with the effects of light on form, a problem which has traditionally been resolved in pigments of strong value contrasts on a surface of intermediate tone. So great was Ingres' preoccupation with light that in conjunction with the colored papers he abandoned his most artful tool, line, and worked almost entirely in terms of tone. This is especially notable in the study for *Virgil Reading from the "Aeneid"* (No. 21).

In his working drawings Ingres was as varied and flexible, if a little less novel, in his choice of media as of papers, and as ingenious and purposeful in their combination. He used all the conventional media of his time: ink, pencil, chalks, crayon, charcoal, and watercolors, both transparent and opaque. Through them he constantly differentiated physical substances, as in his use of pencil for flesh and charcoal for cloth in the drapery studies of Mme. d'Haussonville and Virgil in *The Apotheosis of Homer.* One sees in the variety of media his examination of representational problems in every aspect, modifying and combining them in order to carry through various limited investigations for a single project: the investigation of light, as in the soft pencil and white chalk study of the head of Octavia (No. 22), of composition in the hard pencil and grey wash study for *Virgil Reading from the "Aeneid"* (No. 20), and of form in the blunt, hard pencil and white chalk studies of the hands of the Comte Molé. One sees his willingness to attempt any combination of media that will produce the desired effect, as in the study of the hand of the Duc d'Orléans, which represents in its final state an extremely complex interweaving on slick and textured paper of pencil, chalk and charcoal, applied with a point and by stumping. The usefulness to Ingres of the working drawings, here and elsewhere, takes precedence over harmony of surface. The marriage of the various media seems forced, awkward, and even unattractive at times, as, for instance, in the drapery study for *The Apotheosis of Napoleon* (No. 103). Yet for the artist's intentions, it succeeds.

Turning to the *View of Rome from the Villa Medici* (No. 7), an incidental sketch conceived neither as a finished work nor as a preparatory study, we are struck by its elementary technique. It is a wove sheet, probably a page from a notebook, covered with the briefest unaccented pencil notations. There is only one medium, consistently applied, with no reworkings and certainly no exercise of great technical ingenuity. In viewing this little sheet in all its simplicity, one is forced to recognize even more dramatically the purposefulness of technique of every drawing in this exhibition. Ingres was at all times the master of his tools, selecting them individually with care, combining them with imagination, and realizing their potential as the servants of his artistic conceptions.

MARJORIE BENEDICT COHN

# PHOTOGRAPHIC SUPPLEMENT

2. VIRGIL READING THE "AENEID," 1819? (see Nos. 20, 21 and 22)
Brussels, Musée Royale (Archives Photographiques)

4. THE APOTHEOSIS OF HOMER, 1827 (see Nos. 57, 58 and 59)
Paris, Louvre (Archives Photographiques)

1. ROMULUS CONQUEROR OF ACRON, 1812 (see No. 12)
Paris, École des Beaux-Arts (Giraudon)

3. ROGER DELIVERING ANGELICA, 1819 (see Nos. 50, 51 and 52)
Paris, Louvre (Bulloz)

5. RAPHAEL AND THE FORNARINA, 1814 (see No. 25)
Cambridge, Fogg Art Museum

6. THE VOW OF LOUIS XIII, 1824 (see No. 54)
Montauban, Cathedral
(Archives Photographiques)

7. THE MARTYRDOM OF ST. SYMPHORIEN, 1834 (see Nos. 60, 61 and 62)
Autun, Cathedral (Bulloz)

8. THE APOTHEOSIS OF NAPOLEON I, 1854
(see Nos. 102 and 103)
Paris, Musée Carnavalet (Bulloz)

9. PORTRAIT OF COMTE MOLÉ, 1834 (see Nos. 75 and 76)
Paris, Private Collection

10. PORTRAIT OF THE DUC D'ORLÉANS, 1842 (see No. 84)
Private Collection

11. PORTRAIT OF LOUIS-FRANÇOIS BERTIN, 1832 (see No. 68)
Paris, Louvre (Archives Photographiques)

12. PORTRAIT OF MADAME D'HAUSSONVILLE, 1845
(see Nos. 85 and 86)
New York, Frick Collection

13. PORTRAIT OF MADAME MOITESSIER, 1856
(see Nos. 95 and 97)
London, National Gallery

14. PORTRAIT OF MADAME MOITESSIER, 1851 (see No. 96)
Washington, National Gallery

15. JESUS AMONG THE DOCTORS, 1862 (see No. 113)
Montauban, Musée Ingres (Bulloz)

16. THE RAPE OF EUROPA, 1865 (see No. 116)
Lenormant illustration after a Greek vase.

# INDEX OF TITLES

This catalogue was composed in Linotype Granjon. The original of this type was cut by Jean Jannon of Paris and Sedan in 1621. Composition by The Anthoensen Press, Portland, Maine. Printed by The Meriden Gravure Company, Meriden, Connecticut.